COWBOYS MAKE BETTER PREACHERS

and other humorous tales of the West

LEO SCHREVEN

COWBOYS MAKE BETTER PREACHERS

and other humorous tales of the West

LEO SCHREVEN

Pacific Press Publishing Association
Boise, Idaho
Oshawa, Ontario, Canada

Edited by Jerry D. Thomas
Designed by Dennis Ferree
Cover and inside illustrations by Mike McCarty
Typeset in 12/14 Esprit

The author assumes full responsibility for the accuracy of all facts and quotations cited in this book.

Printed in the United States of America

Schreven, Leo Anthony, 1961-
Cowboys make better preachers and other humorous tales of the West / Leo A. Schreven.
p. cm.
ISBN 0-8163-1346-6 (paper : alk. paper)
1. West (U.S.)—Social life and customs—Humor. 2. Schreven, Leo Anthony, 1961- —Childhood and youth—Humor. I. Title.
F595.3.S37 1996
978—dc20 96-10570
CIP

96 97 98 99 00 • 5 4 3 2 1

Contents

Dedication

I dedicate this masterpiece of polished journalism to
myself, since everyone else I contacted felt
unworthy to be mentioned. Their modesty has been
such an inspiration to me.
Not really.

It's actually dedicated to my five nieces and nephews:
Jenelle, Greg, Jonathan, Mindy, and Kara.
In the last eight years, your combined mischief, laughter,
innocence, and childhood
brought back hundreds of memories.
Most of which I'm still trying to forget.

Introduction

Welcome to the wonderful world of short humor! My brother and I can't remember ever living without laughing. We grew up together in Colorado, laughing our way through life as two country boys in the Rocky Mountains. I loved cowboying, and we both have always shared a love of the wilderness and nature. I reckon we've always been close.

And so, because of his good looks, charming personality, and unique ability to write great short humor (along with my unfathomable generosity), I asked him to join me in writing this book. He is the author of two chapters, both of which are inferior to mine! Nonetheless, they will make you laugh to tears. Since most of the stories involve my brother, I hope you'll grow to love him as much as I do.

Humor has always been part of my life. I don't know how else to write or talk. It's a unique disease that has no known cure. I need to laugh and smile. Perhaps more Christians need to. Laughter is the jam on the toast of life. It adds to the flavor, keeps it from getting too dry, and makes it easier to swallow. Since there is such a lack of humor in Christian literature, it's my hope that the following pages will make your sides ache and your lips smile—and also share some great Bible principles to live by at the same time.

Now before you dive in, you need to understand several things. First, this book is written with a definite western flavor. I'll always be a cowboy at heart. Since most folk only know me as a conservative preacher in three-piece suits, you'll have to rearrange your mental image. Also, short humor is a *style* of writing. It's important to realize that *while the stories are all true*, there is a *mountain of exaggeration*, and *a deep river full of impossibilities*. The *truth is stretched wider than a Colorado sky*, and there is *wild flavoring spread all over*. Please, don't confuse this style of writing with "lying" or "misleading." These stories are not intended to be taken seriously. They are for enjoyment and for teaching life's most important lessons.

You will find some serious notes too. (That's to keep brother and sister Straightface at peace; God rest their pious souls.) This book is written especially for younger minds. (Admit it, adults, you love to laugh too!) In my frequent travels preaching around the world, I see youth today dealing with broken homes, abuse, and being trapped in cities of concrete and crime. Videos, violence, materialism, and false identities have replaced the simple pleasures of country living, nature, and wholesome fun. It's my hope that this book will lift you above the world you may be in, and in an enjoyable way transport you into a world of laughter and happiness as you learn how to make *right decisions*. That's the most important thing you will ever do in life. Never forget it.

You will meet a number of folk under various names to protect their guilt. Several notable ones are:

"Squirrel." This always refers to my younger brother—my best friend and partner in crime.

"Tweetie." My lovely wife, all four foot, ten inches of her. Short and sweet, hard to beat.

"OPA" (Oh-pah). Dutch name for Grandpa, usually referring to my father who aged prematurely, due to raising me.

Leo Schreven

"OMA" (Oh-mah). Dutch name for Grandma, always referring to my mother, who, after reading this transcript, informed me that I was an adopted child with no genetic ties.

CHAPTER

1

Rattle - snakes

In the beginning, God cursed the snake. He must have done a pretty good job of it, since I can't think of a more despised critter in the world today. Rattlesnakes especially.

I hate rattlesnakes. They have a lousy way of improving your reflexes. I know, because during my formative years (or until approximately age thirty), I have improved my reflexes by nearly 400 percent.

Colorado has rattlesnakes like a plague. As my brother and I grew up there, we were always encountering the critters, especially in the summer.

One of my most ancient memories recalls one lovely summer afternoon in Colorado. School was out, and the lure of mountain solitude called constantly to my restless soul. After inhaling a quick lunch that day, my wandering foot got to itching. So I scratched it by saddling up my favorite pony, Ko-Ko. This was a daily ritual as Ko-Ko and I set off for another adventure in the mountains.

That day we were headed for our favorite spot in the west pasture. There, a small clear spring fed a beautiful mountain meadow pond full of life forms yet unknown to science. Ko-Ko would noisily drink after the long uphill climb, and we would compete in water fights. While I threw water in his face, he would kick it back with his hoof. He was a great pony.

Most intriguing, however, was the abundance of waterdogs that swam in the clear water. These were rather ugly amalgamations from before the Flood that looked like overgrown tadpoles with front feet. While Ko-Ko contentedly ate the tender grass, I'd whittle the hours away chasing the water dogs. They made great bait for bass fishing.

When I dumped each one into the bucket, they would burp and grovel their disgust at me. Their angry little eyes looked up so earnestly and made me feel so bad I would finally have to put the lid on the bucket. Selling them for five cents each helped my meager existence at the time.

That fine day, as we made our way up the mountain, the summer's warmth filled us. Ponderosa pine perfume hung rich and sweet in the calm mountain air. Wildflowers dotted the trail as butterflies and bees darted about. The rich savor of horse sweat and leather mingling with the slow, steady creak of the saddle was deeply satisfying. My favorite dog, BeBe, trotted along-side chasing rabbits, horned toads, and the like.

Then it happened. Ko-Ko's flopping ears suddenly perked up, and in that brief instant, I knew all tempest was about to bust loose. Since my eyes were in the middle of a blink, I missed the reaction, but let the record show it went something like this:

Ko-Ko emitted a terrific bellow, hit the panic button, and leapt straight into the air, executing a rolling figure eight with a full twist. While he was turning his ole belly right up to the sun, I left the saddle in a series of flips that would have instantly qualified me for the Olympic gymnastic team. I approached the ground in what appeared to be a full-motion simulation of a 1,000-pound jackhammer.

While still spinning in the sky, Ko-Ko lined himself up to head south for Mexico. As soon as his hooves touched ground, he was off like a bolt of lightning. As for myself, I hammered back on earth and bounced to hit twice more. My glasses fell off, the fillings in my teeth popped loose, and I bit the dust–using my nose for a brake to skid to a stop. My condition was similar to that associated with a German sausage in need of recall.

Midway through these problems, I managed to unlock my eyelids and saw the cause of all the commotion. Three feet away from what used to be my nose was the ugliest rattlesnake I've ever seen. His diamond head swayed back and forth. His evil eyes looked crossed and slightly irritated. He had probably never seen a German sausage in need of recall before.

"Ko-Ko must have stepped on him," I mused, trying hard not to move. As we eyeballed each other, he kept sticking out his tongue at me. It was quite rude. I wanted to tell him to play with his rattles somewhere else but controlled the urge until I could give him an attitude adjustment.

After a few tense minutes, the rattler slowly began to back off, and with enough space between us, I eased back as well, a cold sweat enveloping me in the July heat.

A few rocks later, the snake's anatomy was adjusted (beheaded), and I held the prized rattle in my hand. A fine specimen it was, ten links in all. I proudly put it in my shirt pocket and began to search for my horse and dog. BeBe had long since disappeared and was probably now on the highway trying to hitch a ride back home. Ko-Ko I found a few miles away contentedly munching grass as if nothing had happened. After I stiffly climbed back in the saddle, we slowly made our way back down the mountain.

Reaching into my shirt pocket, I took out the prized rattle. Admiring it with satisfaction, I shook it proudly. Ko-Ko's ears shot up, and the last thing I remember while being airborne was the sight of Ko-Ko's back end as he headed back toward Mexico. It's no wonder my father says that all during my formative years, I went around looking like a commercial for Band-Aids! Those rattlesnakes kept Johnson & Johnson in business.

Another fine spring day, I went out to paint a picture of Longs

Peak. This twin-peaked mountain loomed over 14,000 feet into the blue Colorado sky above our home. It was a constant source of awe and inspiration. Its rugged snowcapped peak held a special fascination for us all. A body can just sit back for hours drinking in the beauty of the Rocky Mountains.

A range of foothills near our home offered an exceptional view of the peaks. Climbing this range was tough, but the reward at the top was worth it all. Mule deer were as thick as sagebrush–I often saw fifty or more in a day. Rabbits and coyotes bounded along with me, and in the spring the wildflowers and sage filled the air with fragrance–God's creation at its finest!

My painting career was limited, due to the common ailment of most artists. They can't convince onlookers that "this is really a tree, and that's a dog, and these are flowers!" How people failed to recognize in my art what was so obvious is beyond me. They say, "Beauty is in the eyes of the beholder," which helps explain why Pearle Vision centers are now popping up all over. I'm convinced most folks can't see straight.

My oma, however, had great eyes. She was able to see wondrous things.

"Oh," she would exclaim, "That's a wonderful portrait you drew of your father!" (It was really Gary Gilmore, a notorious killer.)

Oma could even see things I couldn't, like flowers that were really fence posts, boys who were girls, and vice versa. Oma should have been an art show judge. I'd be a millionaire.

What especially puzzled me was the new, modern art that was so big in the sixties and seventies. It seemed an artist could squeeze out a few tubes of paint, brush it around in a sloppy mess, and let it sit while onlookers "oooed" and "ahhhhed" at what often resembled the cow pies in our north pasture.

I remember one such artist Squirrel and I went to see at a local mall. Trying hard to understand the globs of color, I asked the artist, "What is it?"

His five minute philosophical answer meant little to two country boys. When I told him so, his blood pressure went up fifty points.

"Don't you see? This is an expression of myself; this is how I feel!"

Squirrel and I shook our heads in disgust. If a person felt *that* way, why would they want anyone to know?

At any rate, it made for a good joke. Squirrel and I thereafter would solemnly get out our canvas, squeeze out paint, arrange it like a cow pie, and with great flair come up with masterpieces. Picasso would have been jealous.

And so, inspired by a lovely spring day, I swung all my painting gear on my back, staggered back a few steps, caught my balance, and started off to the ridge. I was going to paint Longs Peak. If it didn't turn out, I'd call it modern art. Life sure was easy.

Crossing over the ridge, I carefully went around some sheer cliffs toward a small ravine. A more peaceful day I'd never known, until my serenity was suddenly shattered. I stepped on a huge rattlesnake.

The poor critter was probably enjoying the sunshine and didn't know what happened either. We both reacted. He rattled and struck my boot. At the same instant, I felt something rubbery move under my foot, and I went into orbit!

"*Yeeeeoowwweeeee!!!*"

I landed in the ravine, barely clearing one side and scraping dirt on the other. I banked high on the rock wall and raced down the narrow canyon. Five hundred yards later, the adrenaline ran out, and I chugged to a stop. The whole event took approximately three seconds.

In that short time, I had collided with my dog, and the result was multiple bites on the legs, neck, and hindquarters. But after a good deal of rest and medication, the dog managed to pull through. Poor thing should have known better than to get in my way.

After dispatching the rattler, BeBe and I slowly walked home. While nervously poking every rock and bush with a large stick, we inched our way along under the blazing summer sun. My battered cowboy hat resembled the year-old remains of a high speed collision between a windshield and a grasshopper. It was miserable, but the buzzards circling overhead did offer some shade and comfort.

Needless to say, the masterpiece was never completed. That's rattlesnakes for you. I spent the rest of the day making more commercials for Band-Aids.

My chief claim to fame in my early years was the uncanny ability to take a bad situation and make it worse. No one understood this better than my beloved younger brother, Squirrel.

While hiking along one day, we decided to scale the red cliffs in front of our home. En route I sent Squirrel ahead to scout, which was really just an excuse to let him reach any nearby rattlesnakes first. Which he did. After almost getting bitten by "ole Diamond Back," Squirrel was just slightly paranoid, a common mental condition that occurs after contact with rattlers. I consider myself an expert in this field and have treated many victims suffering from this dismal condition.

After terminating the snake's miserable existence, we hiked on to the top of the cliffs. As we slowly crawled to the edge, we peered over to stare down sixty feet, into the eyes of what appeared to be a big pussy cat with hair sticking out of its ears.

"Big tomcat Leo. What's it doing up here?" Squirrel asked.

"That ain't no tomcat, Squirrel. That's a bobcat!"

"Tom's cat or Bob's cat, what does it matter . . . Did you say a bobcat?" Squirrel's already paranoid eyes grew wider.

"Yea, Squirrel, a bobcat."

"Ain't them cats dangerous?" Squirrel's lower lip trembled.

"Yeah, they especially like little boys for supper, just like rattlers do."

Squirrel was growing more paranoid by the moment. I forgot to mention that we were between the bobcat and a little gray squirrel (not to be confused with my brother, who wasn't usually gray). Somehow this little squirrel had got himself stuck on a ledge of the cliff and couldn't go left, right, or up—only down into the bobcat's waiting fangs. The little fellow sure was glad to see us and chattered a stream of "Thank yous" for saving his life!

The bobcat wasn't so happy though. Angry that we were intruding between it and a free meal, it hissed and took a few steps forward toward us.

"Are you nervous?" I whispered to Squirrel.

"Not at all," he quipped back.

"Good, then maybe you should let go of my leg. You're cutting off my circulation!"

Without warning, the bobcat lunged toward us, and I heard a most awesome scream. Next, a large animal bolted down the mountain, breaking branches, sending rocks flying, bounding over logs, smashing its way through thickets, grunting, snorting, and wheezing. After several seconds, I realized that that animal was Squirrel.

I found him home awhile later. Poor guy. Too much stress can really age a person. I tried to explain that it wasn't my fault, but it's a bit hard to talk to someone who has rattler-itis. The crossed eyes and twitching is bad enough, but their speech is such that angels blush. They look at you slanchwise, as if somehow it was all your fault. It's best to leave them alone in their room, making sure you bolt and nail the doors and windows for the next twenty-four hours. This usually cures the worst cases.

I learned another important lesson from rattlesnakes. One of our neighbors decided to raise hogs on his place. My good friend, Scott, and I were intrigued by his great big Iowa hogs. But since Mr. Gibbs wasn't the friendliest neighbor you ever met, he didn't like us playing around the hog pens.

We tried to plead innocence, but it's a bit hard when you've been caught throwing pebbles at your neighbor's hogs. He couldn't comprehend that for two thirteen-year-old boys, there isn't too much more enjoyable than throwing a pebble at a hog and listening to it squeal. We also found, to our amazement, that a slingshot was very helpful in producing a longer lasting squeal—often an octave higher.

Each day, on the way home from school, we followed the canal that took us by Mr. Gibbs' hog pens. After carefully selecting our pebbles, we would position ourselves behind granite boulders, toss rocks, and laugh at the grunts and squeals. It wasn't very nice, but two country boys didn't know any better.

One fine day while entertaining ourselves, a movement near the hog pen caught our attention. A closer observation revealed that a fat rattlesnake had taken up residence there. We quickly learned that our pebbles had little impact on his future and that there were no good-sized rocks nearby. After discussing this unfortunate situation, Scott began an earnest search for serious dispatching material.

Just about then, Mr. Snake decided he'd better make a run for the border. But he got his directions mixed up and went north, across the wrong border into the hog pen. I wasn't sure why he did this, since people are generally nicer to snakes than hogs are. But then again, everyone's got to live with their choices.

At about the halfway point across the hog pen, one big sow caught sight of the rattler. Like greased lightning, she was on top of Mr. Snake and in an instant had him between her teeth. That produced a quick reaction! Mr. Snake struck that sow with great force. It bit her eyes, ears, and snoot. Miss Piggy paid no attention, and before my eyes, *ate* that rattlesnake alive!

I stood in total shock. Scott's heavy breathing and armful of rocks jolted me back to reality.

"Where's the snake?" Scott panted.

"Uhh . . . O . . . I mean . . . Well, it ain't here."

"Did you let it get away?" Scott seemed a bit upset.

"Nooo, not exactly . . ."

"Then where is it?"

"Why don't you ask the pig, I think she's got it–or had it; maybe she still has it, sort of, really Scott, I think we're in deep trouble."

Bad images began to creep into my mind. Images like Mr. Gibbs coming to my Opa and demanding payment for his rattlesnake-poisoned hog. My mind raced. *Let's see, that hog is worth $450! My allowance is fifty cents a week . . . almost three years to pay it off!*

This awesome thought, however, was superseded by an image of Opa and his famous belt. Forget about losing my allowance, I was about to lose my hide again . . . for the 431st time.

With troubled and sorrowful minds, we hid behind the granite boulders, waiting in suspense.

"How long till she dies?" Scott asked.

"Don't reckon I know . . . The snake bit her a lot of times. It shouldn't take too much time."

After twenty minutes, the sow lay down.

"This must be it." I said. Scott wanted to be sure. He threw a pebble, and Miss Piggy suddenly came to life! After trotting around for another fifteen minutes, she lay down again.

"This has got to be the end," I said again. We threw another pebble. With a grunt and squeal, the hog trotted away again!

Scott scratched his head. "Hardy hogs,don't you think?"

After several hours of this, our puzzled minds suddenly woke up. Something Oma and Opa and church had taught us finally became clear. The hog is unclean! There's more poison in the hog than in the rattlesnake! And so it was. Miss Piggy was and remained in fine condition.

God knows these things. The food the hog eats, the filth of the land, could go into our bodies as food secondhand. I don't know how you feel, but that ole rattlesnake doesn't sound so appetizing secondhand. In fact, it doesn't sound too good firsthand! In fact, neither the hog or the snake sound good. I'm glad God told us to keep our bodies, as His temple, pure and holy and not to defile them.

In the Bible God describes Satan as a snake. Soon, Satan–the devil, the old serpent-will be crushed forever. In this world, we've got rattlesnakes *and* the serpent, Satan, to deal with. Both can harm you. Both are crafty if you're not on guard. You need to deal with the old serpent, Satan, and temptation the same way we dealt with dangerous rattlesnakes. Just kill them! When Satan comes to tempt you, stone him with the Rock of Ages, and tell him to go to . . . well, he knows where.

CHAPTER

Going Fishing

When Jesus selected His twelve disciples, He made sure there were several fishermen. They were lousy fishermen, as most are today. Every time Jesus met them, they were either mending their nets or whimpering about how the local Gentile fishing corporations were leaving them fishless.

Jesus, on the other hand, was a great fisherman. Every time He went out, He caught tons of fish. Even after His resurrection, He went fishing and treated His disciples to a fish fry by the sea.

Remember the day Jesus was audited by the IRS? Not wanting to offend them, He told Peter to go fishing. "Throw in a hook and line, and the first fish up will have money where his mouth is," Jesus said. "Pay the IRS, and let's move on."

No doubt, Jesus could have done a miracle and provided the money at that moment. However, He must have sensed that Peter was getting tired of fishing for men and needed a day off to relax and fish. So Jesus did it that way. Jesus was like that.

There's a little fishing in all of us—even my little Tweetie. In our boat she sunbathes, reads, and does needlepoint. Mostly, she keeps me honest.

Pulling out a hefty walleye that must weigh at least ten pounds always brings the same response.

"Now, Leo, that fish is so small you could use it for bait to catch a *real* fish!"

Honestly, folks, let me assure you—there's nothing that astounds a fisherman more than someone in the boat who refuses to engage in the mutual exchange of illusions, or someone who tells the simple truth, unstretched, unvarnished, unembellished, and complete! So far, I haven't been able to teach Tweetie this art of exaggeration.

Once in awhile, Tweetie will reel in a few fish, but she won't touch them. "They're slimy and smell fishy," she says, with her little nose turned up.

Then there are times when I lose fish.

"Tweetie, did you see the size of that monster? That would have been a new world record; we could have been millionaires!" Tweetie just smiles and tells me to reread Revelation 21:8 to see where all liars go. The only lesson I've learned from this so far is, "Even a fish wouldn't get caught if it just kept its mouth closed!"

Another amazing phenomenon often occurs when we go fishing together. I catch very few fish. (The real reason I catch so few fish is that I'm a true conservationist.) When I try to share this inside information with Tweetie, she understands. However, I still think it's quite unladylike for her to display her understanding by squealing with laughter and holding her sides.

Still, Tweetie loves to go out fishing with me. Beautiful, mysterious women find it impossible to resist dedicated fishermen. Actually, dedicated fishermen find it impossible to resist a beautiful, mysterious woman—which explains, truthfully, why I catch so few fish with Tweetie on board.

I grew up fishing. Squirrel and I would go to Lake Pleasant near home. Here our careers as fishermen began with bluegills. Standing on the dock peering down into the clear mountain water, we could see hundreds of them. As fast as we could drop a hook with a salmon egg on it, we would have a fish on.

A few hours and several hundred fish later, we advanced to step two. The fish received free high-diving lessons. It's most amazing to witness the ability of these fish! Holding one up as high as his eyes, Squirrel would let it go. With amazing skill, the bluegill dove into the water headfirst, while the other fish in the family below looked up in envy. This was obvious to us, since so many of the fish's relatives were willing to be caught.

Squirrel began advance classes in stunt flying. A bluegill's unique ability to spin in the air at 200 rpm was dazzling, although the landings were a bit rough. This probably explained why, after an hour of lessons, there were a number of cross-eyed fish, belly up, trying to find their bearings.

It was in Colorado, however, that our fishing careers really took off. With the Thompson River out our front door and an irrigation canal out back, we became experts. It all began one spring day when Opa taught us the ropes.

"First, you've got to dig some big, fat, juicy worms. Here is a great place, Leo. You can use my new shovel."

"Wow, thanks a lot!" I replied.

I spaded half an acre of ground and dug worms with great care, selecting only those that showed qualities of endurance, courage, and willingness to sacrifice themselves to a great cause. The next day, while Opa planted his garden in the half acre, Squirrel and I went fishing. When we returned, we each had our limit of fish and an apparently permanent odor—similar to high tide at the cattle yard. We had to be careful passing our neighbor's home—his retirement funds were all invested in the care and feeding of an army of cats. If those kitties ever caught a whiff of us, we would have to high-tail it or become cat chow!

I usually took the precaution of putting a few extra worms in my shirt pocket for future fishing. A wise plan to be sure, until the day my spares were discovered by Oma on washday. You may consider it a scientific fact that dehydrated worms cannot be reconstructed after two cycles in a new washer with bleach. In fact, it's almost impossible to reconstruct a mother who conducts the experiment!

After such an experiment, it is very wise to steer clear of Oma, go out to eat, and in the unlikely event Oma calls you to eat, to first feed supper to your horse and observe the animal carefully for a few hours afterward. I owe my longevity to following this advice.

Fishing became a daily obsession. Every day after school, we would rush to get to our gear as Oma's clear voice rang out. "Now, boys, before you go fishing, you've got to clean your room! It smells like something died in there!"

Actually, it had died on the highway a few days before, but this was no time to argue the details. We would clean our room and head out, determined to be the world's greatest fishermen, make millions, and live a life of ease.

We tried hard to imitate the city-slicker fishermen with their $300 featherweight fly-casting poles. Such a setup was completed with hip waders, and an arsenal of 300 hand-tied flies. Being poor, we settled for two-and-a-half-dollar fly rods and used hip waders from the local Salvation Army. It was miserable. Trout are too smart to eat a hook with a mess of yarn, feathers, and thread that is supposed to resemble a fly. If I were a fish and saw it coming, I'd call 911 and report a UFO (underwater flying object). Besides that, the hip waders were clumsy. Falling into the river instantly filled them with freezing water, while you got dragged through an underwater boulder field.

Our lifelong ambition to be famous fishermen became reality one day in Aspen when we became instant celebrities. While fishing Maroon Creek without any luck, we happened to see a grasshopper jump into the clear water. A second later, a huge trout zoomed out of the depths and exploded on the hopper. Squirrel and I looked at one another in disbelief.

"Grasshoppers!"

Groping around, we quickly caught another one and threw it in the same place. Instantly, the same fish inhaled it.

With great glee, we ran back to camp, grabbed an old mayonnaise jar and began to catch hoppers.

"How many we got now, Leo?" Squirrel was dancing with excitement.

"I reckon about fifteen, Squirrel."

I gazed with wonder at our newest discovery. The hoppers glared back at me, their little eyes filled with accusation.

With a small bobber, we went back to the creek. My hands shook as I prepared our first grasshopper. With the stealth of a mountain lion, we crept to the edge of the creek. Ever so slowly, I cast the hopper into the pool. The same trout struck like a bolt of lightning and a moment later was flopping on the bank.

"Squirrel, we done got us a secret nobody knows!"

In less than an hour, we each had our limit of eight fish. We walked proudly back to our tent, making sure to go by as many campers as possible. Fishermen inquired as to what we were using.

Squirrel was quick to answer. "You'll never guess! We caught 'em all on grasshhhh . . ." at which point he stopped short. He calmly gave a more reasonable explanation after he pried my fingers off his throat.

"Did you say grass, son?" one of the campers inquired.

"Yea, nice green grass, about four- to six-inches long. Thread it on a hook, and it looks like a worm swimming in the water."

OK, maybe that wasn't nice, but one good thing came from it. The campground was neatly mowed by hundreds of hopeful fishermen plucking grass. The National Park Service should have awarded us a bronze star for our ingenuity.

After that, Squirrel and I became expert grasshopper catchers. Hoppers didn't hop so good early in the morning, due to the cold, so we'd be out shortly after sunrise. It didn't take long to catch the whole day's supply.

We especially prized the "American Hoppers," as we called them. They were a strange breed–colored red, white, and blue. In the cool Colorado mornings, they were rare, but you could find about one an hour. These went into a special jar reserved only for our best fishing holes.

Our philosophy of fishing was simple. "The two best times for fishing is when it's raining, and when it ain't."

Our daily excursions to the Thompson River yielded many a fine trout. Since Oma's freezer was already packed to the hilt, we would occasionally have our own fish fry on the river. We always said that's when fish tasted the best, anyway. Caught fresh, cooked with a little salt, a bucket of butter, some ashes and sand, and eaten with your grubby fingers. Life doesn't get any better for two country boys.

We fished mainly for trout, but we also caught a lot of suckers. These were useless fish and were quickly discarded. They did put up a good fight, though. We felt justified discarding them, knowing the local racoons or bears would have a free dinner.

We were also the proud discoverers of many a new fishing hole. For instance, the famous Mill Creek hole. From Pinewood Lake in front of our home flowed a small creek that was hardly noticed. You had to climb the mountain and descend to the valley to find the creek. It was a wild area, and few, if any, ever went there.

During one of our adventure hikes, we accidentally stumbled onto this creek. It was only three feet wide in most places, with pools here and there. Squinting into the first pool, we saw trout spook in every direction. Don't laugh, you would spook, too, if you ever saw my brother's face.

Running back home for our poles, we fished only a hundred yards of the creek and had more trout than we could carry!

"What's the limit on these fish?" Squirrel asked.

"Eight fish each for twenty-four hours."

"Don't you reckon we ought to count them? I think we're over the limit." Squirrel asked as he drug four full stringers of fish behind him.

This was the last thing I ever wanted to hear. Limits! Ugh! I hated limits! Over the years, I'd wore out fish trying to count them to make sure I was not "over the limit." It was a real pain for a country boy, especially for one who didn't have a better grasp of mathematics than I did. Game wardens were always sneaking up on you and wanting to count your fish. It was enough to keep you in fits of the "jearvous nerks."

As I grew older, my fishing career progressed. From my two friends Steve and Robert, I've learned that getting your Ph.D. requires less work than becoming an average fisherman. New technology in the fishing world has resulted in amazing gear like space-age, ultralite graphite rods. So light, in fact, that my friend Steve once made seven casts before realizing he hadn't picked up his rod yet!

I now own a bass boat, fish locator, eleven graphite rods and reels, two tackle boxes full of stuff I never use, trolling motors, fishing glasses, color charts, buzz baits, spinner baits, crank baits, plastic worms you stuff with Alka-Seltzer—you name it, I got it. I look back with envy to those good ole days with a two dollar fiberglass rod, an old Zebco reel, and an American hopper.

At the tender young age of twenty, I was struck down with the necessity of having to take on a real job. As a result, my fishing has been severely limited to weekends, nighttime, between crusades, Christmas, Thanksgiving, summer breaks, and in my dreams. I now have to plan each trip with great care. Sadly, the good ole days are gone.

Lately, however, my fishing fever has spread to my relatives. Even my brother John got caught up in the excitement.

John's a good ole boy who makes his living playing with other people's money. We were a bit far apart in age so never did much of anything together. He also had a problem. Fishing takes a lot of concentration, and John couldn't concentrate on anything longer than fifteen seconds, unless it wore a dress and smelled like perfume. He was interested in weird things like city living, theater plays, sports, and such. For some reason smelly horses and cows had no appeal to him. He couldn't see why fish were so exciting. A mountain is to be driven over, not hiked, and his idea of roughing it was sleeping overnight in the Phoenix Sheraton. Not wanting him to end up as a criminal, drug addict, or a golfer, I felt it my duty to save John by introducing him to fishing.

John was finally enamored enough by my pictures and stories of red fish in Louisiana that he finally flew into New Orleans to join me for a grand three-day fishing excursion.

We drove down to the bottom of the earth, south of New Orleans, to what they call "Cajun Country." (A Cajun, by the way, is any person in the south who is quick enough to grab the food off his plate before it crawls back into the water.)

Upon our arrival at the most modern inn available, I could see John was having his doubts.

"Lookie here, John! Twin beds! You can have the newer one with the customized dip in the center. I tell you what, John, this ain't no downstream motel. Check out this TV! Black and white with two channels!"

John elected to hit the shower instead of me, and I was beginning to think all was well—then he came out with his eyeballs barely hanging onto his head.

"There, there, th-there's a gr . . . gre . . . green lizard in there who watched me take a shower!"

"Was it a male or female green lizard?" I asked. He didn't seem to think it mattered. "Well, this is Cajun Country, John. It's filled with mosquitoes and gnats, so the dee-lux rooms like this one come complete with a green lizard to keep it bug free. Now quit broadcasting it, or everyone else is gonna want one!"

That seemed to satisfy him. At least, he stopped asking about it.

The next day, we began our fishing, and I must admit that John had a definite knack for it. You see, he's left-handed, and left-handed people are the only ones in their right minds. This explains why he caught a bunch of fish. All was going great until day two.

We were cruising along on our way out to the gulf when we accidentally ran up on a shell reef. The sea was rough, the waves were high, and water began to crash into the boat. With the nearest land two miles away, we had to handle it ourselves. So we bailed out most of the water, pushed the boat off the reef, and hit the bilge pump.

That left just enough water in the boat to cover John's 35mm camera and accessories. I felt really bad about that, because I really wanted a picture of John's face when he discovered it. But the hurricane blast created by John's few appropriate remarks kept me busy trying to keep us afloat!

I wasn't completely successful. As the water continued to crash into the boat, a cold chill shot through me. Not only was John in extreme danger, he was also still carrying the communal bait can.

"Quick," I yelled, "toss me the can." Needless to say, the bait was saved. John was rebaptized against his will several times but came out a truly changed man.

By the third day, John was doing fine. He was beginning to look like a normal person. The three-day cactus patch on his cheeks looked great. His lily-white face was sunburned, and his ears were peeling. He smelled like a dead fish instead of aftershave, and his hands were all cut, cracked, and swollen from fish scales and salt water. His Levis were dirty and his baseball cap muddy. His tie would have looked the same, but I told him the locals wouldn't understand him wearing it, so he wisely left it back at the hotel.

After such a wonderful trip, it was tough to say goodbye at the airport. John has since told me over and over that he can't wait to go again. Unfortunately, something always comes up. First his car broke down, then he injured his arm, next his mom died, and so on. I sure hope his bad fortune ends soon so we can go out again.

Opa, however, is the exact opposite of John. I can't keep him away from fishing! The other day, I went out alone to enjoy a relaxing getaway. Suddenly, Opa was beside me in the boat, casting into my personal fishing hole.

"Where did you come from?" I asked in astonishment.

"Well, son, I was just down here working on your boat battery when you drove off and I couldn't get out. No problem. Why, look, my rods, reels, tackle box, and lunch are here too! Isn't that amazing! I might as well stay for a while."

Really, Opa is my best fishing buddy—next to Tweetie, that is. Opa and I have made a lot of memories together—most of which he is still trying to forget.

For instance, that fateful day on the Kettle River in Washington comes to mind. While building on my house, we just got tired one afternoon and decided to go fishing instead. Since Oma had just bought us new life jackets for our birthdays, we needed an excuse to break them in. Oma was insistent that we wear the life jackets at all times. My exegesis of what a safe, sensible, and careful captain I was didn't seem to make much of an impression on her. I've learned that there are only two theories about arguing with a mother, and neither one works.

The Kettle River flows down into the Columbia River near our home. In the lazy days of summer, the mighty Columbia rises eighty to a hundred feet above its normal winter height. This is because our Canadian friends across the border send us all their snow after it thaws. The Grand Coulee Dam downriver contributes to this rise also.

Because of this rise in water height, the Columbia waters back up into the Kettle River gorge several miles in the summer. This creates a placid lake, smooth as velvet, for the last two miles of the Kettle River.

Opa and I put in about six miles up the Kettle and began our float down to the Columbia. We had floated there many times the previous summer, but this was our first trip in the spring. While catching walleye, trout, bass, and whitefish, we noticed the river was a bit rough. But who could worry with fish jumping on our lines on nearly every cast?

Approaching a sharp bend in the river, I finally noticed a change of scenery.

"This place look familiar, Opa?"

Opa was preoccupied with another fish.

A dark, rocky canyon rose up slowly on each side.

"Funny I don't recall this place, Opa. Looks like the Grand Canyon. Did we miss a turn?"

Opa grunted something about how nice it was to be up to our arms in fish.

While contemplating nature's phenomenon, it suddenly dawned on me this area had been under eighty feet of water the last time we had floated down. I awoke with a start to observe that the momentum of the river had increased considerably. A strange noise, similar to a freight train, grew louder and louder.

As we rounded the next bend, I looked up in wonder to see what appeared to be an upside-down waterfall. Opa and I both yelled, but the thunderous sound drowned out everything else. We churned the river into butter trying to paddle back upstream, but the current sucked us into its narrows.

With the white water just about upon us, I got out a can and started bailing as fast as I could. We weren't taking any water over the sides yet, but the bottom of the boat was full of cold sweat.

When we hit the first rapid, the boat trembled and filled with water. About the time we cleared our glasses, we hit the next one. Opa was saying something about the pearly gates when suddenly I couldn't find my boat. For that matter, I couldn't find Opa, either. In fact, I couldn't even find the sunshine!

I will not attempt to tell you what shooting that rapid was like. About the fishing poles snapping in our hands like matchsticks, the drop-offs, the drop-ups, the part where we were walking horizontally along the cliffs, the part where the boat was on top of us and the whole river was on top of the boat–I certainly won't tell you about the bad parts. It will suffice to say that when we finally emerged, we were 300 yards downstream in freezing water from the last ice age.

Opa was hung up on a rock on one side of the river, and I stumbled out on the other side. Poor Opa was in shock, and we just about lost him. But help was nearby, and everything turned out OK. The boat was never found. It was either pulverized or some fish is using it for a luxury condo down on the bottom of the river.

Oma's life jackets had saved the day for us. Now for our next birthday, I've requested a jacket for our new boat, just in case we see more of those upside-down waterfalls.

One nice thing about fishing is that no matter where you go, you can always find water with fish in it–unless you live in New York City where the water's too thick for fish to swim in. I've been fortunate enough to travel a lot in evangelism and fish along the way. Colorado trout, Florida bluefish, Louisiana redfish, Texas speckled trout, Missouri bass, Georgia gar, Washington walleye, Idaho pike,

Arizona bluegill, Canadian grayling, and Alaskan king salmon—each is unique and has to be fished for differently.

It's like fishing for men and women. Across the earth are many wonderful varieties of people. Trying to catch them can be an exciting and rewarding challenge. God needs some good fishers of people! Some are easy to find and fish for, like bluegills. Some are hard to reel in, like a tarpon. Some are pretty, some not so pretty, some weak, some strong, but like fish, people are all over the earth. No matter where you go, you can find them—men and women hungry for what you have to give them. God wants all of us to be fishers of people.

Many today use their talents to make money and have an easy life. That's not what we are here for. I want to challenge you to be a fisher of people. Work to pay expenses, but be a soul winner for Christ!

There's someone you can fish for today. Maybe a friend or relative, a schoolmate, or a work associate. Perhaps you can target a neighbor, your insurance agent, or the postal carrier. It's a great way of life, and in the end, you get to enjoy seeing your "fish" put back into the water when it's baptized. Ain't no bigger thrill than that!

CHAPTER

Hug A Logger
(You'll Never Go Back to Trees)

Loggers are a special breed. You can always tell them, but you can't tell them much. With their tin hats, bushy beards, and red flannel shirts, they have a funny habit of running around the woods yelling "Timmmberrr!" Black suspenders hold up britches that have never seen a washer and are always six inches too short. Loggers stand proud and tall in their black cork boots–till a mighty tree falls on them and they waddle away with their legs protruding from their armpits. Hey, they don't mind, they're *loggers!*

The typical logger is often a bit crazy. Take, for example, my good friend Keith. Keith is a true logger in British Columbia, Canada. We roomed together for several years during high school. Keith was the dean and farm manager. I was the "rebellious young whipper-snapper," as he put it. Keith could understand such whipper-snappers because, in reality, he also was one. He was just better at not letting folks know about it. In other words, he knew how to keep his mouth shut, something I have yet to master. Our parents suffered from severe nervous disorders, which created an immediate bond between us.

COWBOYS MAKE BETTER PREACHERS

Our first logging episode took place when I was sixteen and at the height of my intellectual powers at school. We were felling trees on the east slope of Strine Creek, way out in the British Columbia woods. The snow was deep, and me and the boys were having a blast throwing snowballs, while Keith tried to mow down the forest. During the process, we did manage to learn how to run a chain saw, how to oil and clean it, and how to make a tree fall "over there" and not on our heads. After all, a guy with his legs protruding from his armpits isn't too attractive to the young women at school.

We also learned how to saw rocks, an art that Keith never learned to fully appreciate. He was always mumbling something about sharpening chains, rather than admiring our carvings. It's hard to get along with someone who cannot appreciate fine art.

One beautiful day after successfully carving rocks, we were heading back for lunch when we discovered an old car hood near the dump where we were logging. General Motors would be proud to know the hood of its 1940 classic made a perfect sleigh! Attaching a rope to the hood and the other end to the back of Keith's red truck, we took off. It was grand, six guys flying across frozen sugar at thirty miles per hour. The snow billowed up in our faces, blinding our eyes. We were laughing, yelling, choking, and, in general, having a good time as we tore down the mountain approaching the apple orchard. Here, the road took a sharp right turn around the orchard.

Keith had no problem making the corner but momentarily forgot his lessons on the physics of motion. With snow flying, we began a wide arc around the corner, when suddenly we saw in front of us what appeared to be fence posts and barbed wire. Keith's desperate attempt to saw us into four equal sections had almost succeeded.

It wasn't a pretty sight, but it was a nice package–six guys all rolled up like wieners on the car hood, tied up with barbed wire, and ready for delivery at the local hospital. Goose down floated gently in the air from what once was our winter coats, and together with the softly falling snow, made a lovely scene.

It was just the first of many times that Keith tried to kill me.

A few days later, after recuperating, we were back in full swing, logging the mountain. On our way down, Keith suggested we play football with a snowball. The game went great until kick off.

Keith was about as bright as a burned out light bulb.

After hiking the new snowball, I was off and flying down a mountain made of granite boulders–disguised under a blanket of snow. Keith's pass was overthrown, but with a long dive worthy of instant replay, I caught the snowball. I anticipated a graceful fall into the white fluff. Instead, I saw all the stars in the milky way–at 11:30 a.m.–in broad daylight. It made a great impression on Keith but an even greater impression on the granite boulder. The greatest impression was on my knee.

Yyeeeowwwwweeghhh!

With a busted knee cap, I was carted back to the infamous "horse doctor" in a nearby animal hospital and after only a short wait behind more important (animal) patients, got patched up. Did I mention that I continued to be the official spokesman for Band-Aids during high school?

This was just the beginning of sorrows. Once, Keith ran over me with his truck, cracking the bones in my foot. Twice, he tried to kill me in the air. I'd have been safer going to school with a pack of starving wolves.

We were flying to Oregon in a Cessna 172 that Keith had rented. Our plan was to go down there during a school break and make a bunch of quick money by logging. While the plane climbed out over the mountains of British Columbia, I gazed at the beautiful scenery below. It was then I noticed the airplane tire.

"Hey, Keith, how old's this plane?"

He shrugged. "I reckoned twenty or thirty years old."

"When's the last time you changed tires?"

He shrugged again and said, "I don't know. Ain't my plane."

That was reassuring. "What's this plane worth?"

"I reckon $6,000 or so."

"Let's see . . . three people . . . $6,000 . . . that's $2,000 apiece for an airplane casket. Woah!"

"What are you griping about? And what do you mean, a casket?"

"Well, Keith, I hate to make your day, but I got some bad news. The tire on this side ain't got no rubber on it—just an inner tube. How you figure on landing this bird?"

Keith took a look and let out a roar that could best be described in comparison to a polar bear having a tooth extracted without the benefit of an anesthetic or ice. Then he asked me if I knew anything about prayer.

Fortunately, that's something we both knew about. We prayed. No, we begged. In fact, we got on our knees, which I don't recommend when you're flying a small plane. But desperate men do desperate things.

Approaching the airport in Oregon, we had a strong headwind that enabled us to slow down considerably. I could see Keith was getting irritated—his right eye was twitching severely, and he was pacing back and forth popping his knuckles. He always did that when we were in trouble. But upon returning to his seat, Keith carefully maneuvered the plane, favoring the left tire, and amazingly, the inner tube tire held.

The airport mechanic summarized it dryly. "You boys done had someone up there in the sky looking out for you."

On our way out of the airport to the logging camp, Keith was smiling. "Well, I guess things can't get any worse!"

We soon discovered he lacked the gift of prophecy.

A week later on our return trip to Canada, we somehow managed to get a late start. We ended up flying over the rugged mountains of the Frazer Valley as the sun was setting—with forty miles to go. I forgot to mention that the airport we were headed for was an inlet strip of grass and potholes that was used for grazing cattle, deer, and bush pilots who had been flying too long. It sat between the Frazer River and the highwire lines with approximately thirty feet clearance. The darkness crept in, grinning at our foolishness.

"Can you see to land?" I asked, trying to sound casual.

"Got no choice. Nearest lighted airport is in Kamloops, and we ain't got fuel to make it there. Help me look for that patch of grass—it's supposed to be down here somewhere."

All I could see was a lot of darkness. One of the guys in the plane with us, a devout atheist named Pete, was starting to sweat. Above the roar of the motor he yelled, "Do you think we're going to make it?"

"I doubt it, Pete." I replied.

Pete mumbled something about having some recent thoughts of doubting the validity of atheism, but I couldn't really hear him.

As Keith began his descent into the darkness, we approached what appeared to be a field. It's amazing how many things look the same in the dark when you're flying at 120 mph. Peering through the night, we tried to make out something solid to aim at or around.

A nice selection of insects suddenly splattered on the windshield—a fate we seemed destined to share. Suddenly, the airplane lights picked up a new shape, a shape that grew clearer each moment.

"What in the world . . . it looks like . . . must be the . . . a TREEEE!"

Keith performed a hammerhead roll that made my eyes sink down to my navel. I thought about complementing him on the stunt, but as my eyes rolled back into place, I opted to sit back and enjoy the magnificent view of the moon and stars toward which we were now headed. In the back, Pete was now on his knees confessing his sins with tears and anguish.

It was becoming clear that Keith had his heart set on turning my wife into a widow—and I hadn't even had a chance to get married! His mumbling about going down in a blaze of glory didn't encourage us. We were a sorry lot. Keith was holding onto the wheel with white knuckles, Squirrel was crouched on the floor sweating bullets, the dog was navigating, and I was chewing my seventh pack of gum, along with what was left of my fingernails. A few seconds later, Pete swore off smoking, drinking, and profanity, the last of which cut his vocabulary at least in half.

While making our third attempt, we spotted the grass a hundred yards to the left. Keith performed a hard degree turn, and with half the runway already gone, we gracefully touched down—OK, the plane was running all over the field, ripping up sod and scaring rabbits into the next county, but any touchdown at less than a hundred miles an hour seemed graceful at that point.

When the plane finally stopped, Keith was crouched on the floor, Squirrel was navigating, the dog was chewing gum, and Pete announced he had decided to enter the ministry.

Ugghaghh! I spit out a handful of grass. "Is everyone OK?" From where I was wedged up under the dashboard, everyone looked dazed.

"Wow," Keith drooled as he crawled out, "shall we try it again? All we need is a little luck and we could be stunt men!"

"All you need is a good psychiatrist," Squirrel said. The dog kept chewing his gum with a bewildered look, while Pete was already hitchhiking his way to Andrews University.

With Keith's trying to kill me, our logging days were full of excitement. We usually worked for an outfit in Oregon. The boss and his sons were good to us and offered us a trailer in the woods to stay in while working. We should have known better than to accept, since they were loggers.

The trailer was a bit rough. Definitely not a showcase for the local health department. Mice had moved in, so we got a few traps out, cleaned up, and started a fire in the woodstove. It was good to be in the woods. Pure air, fragrant pines, and serenity are things I have always loved. There are no city sounds, just the soft breeze, peace, and quietude. A person can find himself in such a situation. All God's untainted creation can fill your heart. The billions of stars above awe the soul. The swaying of the evergreens relaxes tension. Problems and hassles of life disappear like campfire smoke.

"Ahhhhh . . . this is true contentment!" I remarked.

WWHAAAP!

My daydream was rudely awakened.

WWHAAAP!

Closer inspection revealed that two mice had bit the cheese. Keith reset the traps, and we began to rerelax, telling stories around the woodstove.

WHAP! WHAAP! WHAAAP!

And so it continued all evening. I never saw so many mice! Keith finally asked me to tend the traps while he went to fix some supper. This concerned me far more than the mice did—I'd eaten Keith's cooking before.

After we choked down what Keith said was a "logger's dinner," he proudly brought out a homemade "logger's pie," complete with whip cream. The white topping turned out to be shaving cream, so I ate it—I didn't trust the pie. We finished it off with Keith's country decaf coffee. It came two ways: weak—the spoon stands up by itself; strong—the spoon dissolves.

I opted for the weak.

By eleven o'clock, we figured we had killed every mouse in the county, as well as our own intestines, and decided to go to bed. Drifting off into dreamland, I was suddenly wakened in the night to the most pathetic sound I'd ever heard.

Eeeeek, Aghweeeeeeek! Thud!

"You hear that, Keith?" I asked, petrified under my sleeping bag.

"Hear what?" Keith grumped.

"That 'eeek' sound. Get out your flashlight."

The flashlight revealed nothing.

"You're dreaming, Leo. Hit goose down, and quit bothering me. We got a big day tomorrow."

We drifted off, but suddenly the sound came again, only louder this time, as if something was about to die.

Eeeeek! Thud!

"Did you hear it that time, Keith?"

"Yea. What on earth was it?"

We searched again. Nothing.

Eeeeek! Thud! Eeeeeeeccckk! THUD!

This continued for hours. We both became a bit groggy-eyed.

"Leave the light on awhile," Keith finally suggested. "Let's just sit quiet and look."

After a few minutes, we spotted a little mouse on the kitchen counter. It moved quickly to the edge of the counter near the woodstove.

"Cute little fella," I whispered. "Isn't it, Keith?"

Then the mouse jumped onto the woodstove.

EEEEEEEEK!

The poor little mouse must have been a distant relative of Speedy Gonzales–I've never seen a critter move that fast! It danced on that hot stove top (a polka, I think), flew through the air, hit the floor with a thud, and high-tailed it out of there! Keith was laughing and clapping so hard the mouse came back for an encore.

We didn't get much more sleep, as mouse after mouse got fried feet that night. We went to work the next morning looking like we each had a hangover. The big boss eyed us suspiciously, "You boys up to working this morning?"

"Oh yessir, yessir! Just a bad case of mice . . ." We decided it was better to remain silent and risk the chance of appearing ignorant than to open our mouths and remove all doubt.

Logging is a great job for guys with energy to spare. Had my mother known about it, I would have been employed by age three. That morning, the hardy workers didn't take too kindly to us at first, since we came from doing activities they despised–school, for instance. We didn't really fit in, since we didn't cuss, smoke, drink, kiss, or do anything else bad for health or morals.

The big boss stepped up.

"Allright, boys, business has been slow lately–'bout the last fifteen years. I want you to get out there and hustle. You hear me?"

One of the new loggers responded quickly. "Yes sir, no problem, sir. We underpaid loggers, led by you the uninspiring, into the uncharted, assisted by the unqualified (he looked at Keith and me) have been doing the impossible, with the inadequate (he looked at us again) for so long, that we can now do anything, for anybody, with nothing!"

The boss looked at him slanch wise and said, "You're fired!" And so began our logging careers.

My job was to drive a skidder and haul logs out of the woods. A skidder is an incredible machine with four huge wheels with full-time four-wheel drive, a blade up front, a bunch of gears, a powerful, noisy motor, and the ability to go anywhere at breakneck speed.

Nothing in your path is too much—even small trees just get run over. To qualify as a skidder driver, all you need is an I.Q. of thirty or less, a valid cereal box driver's license, and hands strong enough to hold on—which probably explains why I got the job.

As the fallers sawed down the trees, a bucker would trim off all the branches and cut the logs into forty-foot lengths. These logs were scattered all over the woods. After storming up the mountain, I'd park the skidder and release the back pulley. A long steel cable rolled out, with ten smaller steel cables attached. These cables were called chokers.

Next, I would jump out and run the main cable. Every time I came to a log, I'd wrap a "choker" around it. Working fast, it was possible to set ten chokers in five minutes. Then I'd bail into the skidder, rev the motor, and hit the pulley lever. The main cable would roll in and logs from ten different directions would come crashing together. It was grand! The cable would strain, and the skidder would tremble and shake, all while the motor screamed. Trees and boulders were swept aside or crushed as the massive logs were pulled right up to the skidder.

Then with a "whoop" and a smile, I would cram the skidder into gear, pop the clutch, and tear down the mountain full blast with ten logs on my tail. It was mass destruction at its finest! Upon arrival at the landing, I would bail out, loosen the chokers, zip up the main cable, and go back for more.

The huge logging trucks stood by, waiting. Here is where the "real men" were—the truck drivers. Using the tiny narrow logging roads, they would navigate their massive loads down incredibly steep inclines, within six inches of a sheer cliff on one side and a potential avalanche on the other, in rain, sleet, or snow. They would perform this amazing feat with one foot on the running board, one hand on the wheel, and the other hand clutching a rosary—even the atheists. Eventually, they would arrive at the lumber or pulp mills where the paper this book is printed on comes from. So if you're enjoying the book, thank a logger!

Work varied. Some days, I'd buck logs at the landing, some days

help build new roads. It was always a hazardous job, but at the time, we were too busy or too foolish to notice. Falling trees was especially bad.

Keith was an expert at "falling." In between his frequent falls, he did manage to knock down a few trees. A massive spruce tree, three to four feet through and 150 feet high, is a lot of wood. Keith would notch the side he wanted it to fall on, then begin on the backside cutting a deep line. In this line he would place wedges and drive them deep, ever so slowly tipping the tree in the right direction. It was painfully slow and delicate work. One mistake could cost your life easily. The trunk could slip and send a logger into orbit, or "backfire" when falling, giving you a permanent heart attack.

When at last the tree would teeter, Keith would jerk out his saw, and make tracks to the side. The massive tree would hit the earth with an awesome crash, shaking the ground for a mile in each direction. Keith would grin and shout, "There's another fifty bucks!" With a whoop, he'd begin to saw another.

Things are different now. I sort of get embarrassed when I think of how we trashed the woods. God is good to provide a renewable resource like wood, but like all good things, we have a responsibility to care for it.

Man's greed has led many countries to deplete the very things necessary for life and happiness. Sin has caused us to make a big mess of what used to be a perfect earth. While we await the coming of Christ and the new heavens and earth, we should be faithful stewards of our world and all that's in it. Once it's gone, you can't replace it.

It's a lot like each of us—you and me. God made you in His image and gave you a marvelous body. He told you what to put in it and what not to and how to take care of it. A lot of people make really stupid decisions and put alcohol, drugs, and cigarette smoke in it. They don't exercise, and they eat junk food full of fat instead of nutrition. When they lose their health, they never get it back. Health is wealth, so remember every day to take good care of yourself.

God also gave you dignity and nobility—purity and honor. Precious things. A lot of people make really stupid choices here, too, and squander away all this with premarital sex, adultery, lust, or bad choices in things they see and listen to. You never gain it back. Sin desensitizes you. Make right choices *now.* One good choice will make a lifetime of happiness. One stupid choice will make you a lifetime of hellish misery. God forgives, but He can't change the results of bad decisions.

Choose wisely . . . every day. The most important decision you will ever make in life is to choose to make right decisions.

CHAPTER

Hoss Flesh and Other Hazards

I've always loved horses. They are, in my humble opinion, the most magnificent creatures God created. Horses can become a closer friend to you than some people. President Ronald Reagan once said, "There's nothing better for the inside of a man than the outside of a horse!" I agree.

Through time, the understanding and relationship can grow incredibly deep between a man and his horse. Horses are intelligent, kind, and very sensitive creatures. Their eyes, the largest of any living mammal, can tell of happiness, danger, fear, and mischief. Their ears are an instant communicator. Pointing forward, they convey there is something ahead a human can't see, but the horse can. Laid back, the ears indicate fear or anger–your horse is about to kick, buck, or destroy something nearby! With its beautifully sculptured head, its flowing mane and tail, and its delicate feet, a horse symbolizes a free spirit that's lost in all of us. Not a day's gone by that I wouldn't rather have been with my horse than with most people.

The wonder of seeing a magnificent horse trotting through a field is a mosaic of beauty that captivates the heart and raises a lump in my throat. Sitting astride that horse while galloping across an alpine meadow is enough to make a grown man cry with pleasure. The wind in your face brings a thousand smells you would never encounter otherwise. The quivering strength beneath you sends tingles up your spine. Together, a man and horse can become one unit, a movement of poetry—impossible to write, only to be experienced.

No one has exalted the virtues of horses more than the cowboys of the old West. Every person, preacher, and politician ought to have the privilege to cowboy for a while. It would do wonders for juvenile delinquents. A few days on a cattle ranch will take the conceit out of anyone. It will teach you self-reliance, it will teach you to endure hardship and suffering, it will give you nerve and pluck. It will develop any latent energy into a productive life.

Cowboying is a noble job compared to most. Contrast it, for example, to politics. A cowboy gets up early in the morning, decides what he wants to do, then saddles up his horse and gets to work. He does the best he can and spends as little money as possible.

A politician, on the other hand, gets up late in the morning, straddles the fence, spends all the money he can, gets all his votes lined up, and then decides what to do.

That's probably why Congressman Robert Smith made the following statement in 1994: "The only comparison I can make between moving a bunch of cows across the range and moving a bill through Congress is that if you're behind a bunch of cows you can give them direction, but behind a piece of legislation, it's a free-for-all. So I'm leaving politics. I'm getting out of Washington and going back to my ranch in Oregon, where there's some stability and judgment left in the world!"

Well said, don't you think?

Let me tell you about Bill. Bill was a genuine old cowpoke who lived near us in Colorado. He had true bow-legs from spending years in the saddle, and he spoke with a slight speech impediment. His high-strained voice and peculiar cough were made fun of by the young people, but Bill was a hero to me. Each morning, Bill would go up to his horse with a sack of oats hidden in his jacket. His beloved pinto would always come running. Tickling her chin, Bill would lovingly say, "You ole Roman-nosed bag of bones, how are you this morning?"

The horse would nuzzle Bill as he drawled on, "You know, you ain't worth a dime. I ought to trade you in and let 'em make you into dog food. How would that suit you?"

The pinto would nicker softly as Bill continued, "Naw, I reckon you're still a right fine piece of hoss flesh, might as well keep on feeding ya." With this, he would pull out the oats, and while his horse feasted, Bill would pet her and ramble on. Sometimes Bill drifted off in memories–past days of his cowboy life. His face, weathered by the wind and sun, was a reflection of this life he loved. His hands, gnarled and rough from fence mending and hay bales, became instruments of sensitivity and care around his choice mare.

Bill may not have been the brightest guy you ever met, but he was sincere. There was the time a city greenhorn's car broke down nearby. He walked up to the ranch and met Bill. The conversation went something like this:

Greenhorn: "My car broke down, do you have a monkey wrench here?"

Bill: "Nope. My uncle got a sheep ranch over there, and my boss got a cattle ranch here, but it's too cold for a monkey ranch in these parts."

Bill looked at the greenhorn as though he must have lost his mind.

The greenhorn was just as bewildered: "How about a telephone, then?"

On many an occasion we sat together; I, a young aspiring cowboy who idolized Bill's every word and action; he, an old tough cowhand who was lonely. He taught me how to tie knots, braid a whip, shampoo leather, and most of the other horse sense stuff I know. His language was a bit rough like the rest of him, but his heart was solid gold. Bill taught me a lot of cowboy wisdom and lore. Some of his favorite sayings are worth remembering.

"Son, don't ever squat with yer spurs on!"

He taught me the most important part of getting dressed.

"Son, always wear yer hat. And make sure it has a brim wide enough to shed rain and sun, stiff enough to fan a fire, deep enough to dip water, and hard enough to whip a fightin' cow in the face!"

And he taught me general wisdom.

"Son, don't never interfere with something that ain't bothering you none." Or, "Son, don't take to sawing the branch that's supportin' you, unless of course you're hanging from it!"

And then there were the stories. Bill had plenty, and all of them had a lesson.

"One day," Bill drawled, "I was having trouble with a mountain lion killing my beef. So I decides to track down that big pussy cat and shoot 'im. Twasn't hard fer me. You see, one day that kitty kilt one of my big prize bulls. He done ate the whole thing! After the feast, the kitty felt so good he started to roaring. He kept it up, and I heard 'im and walked right up and introduced myself, Smith and Wesson."

Bill paused and whittled a stick for a while.

"You know the moral of that story, son?" Bill asked.

I shook my head. Bill hunkered down and looked me in the eye. "When you're full of baloney, keep your mouth shut!"

Now honestly, folks, where else can you get an education like that?

One late fall day, Bill and I rode together looking for stray cattle. He rode his beloved mare; I had my favorite pony, Buckey. Buckey was not mine, but the ranch manager allowed me to use him like my own. He was a beautiful paint horse, built like a rock–a true mountain horse. With unlimited energy, he could trot along all day. He had an exceptional sense of direction as well. Miles from home, deep in the mountains, he could be given free rein and without hesitating would pick his way back home. Best of all, he was full of spirit, hence his name "Buckey."

Every morning, Buckey would prance with anticipation while being saddled. I'd cinch the saddle down tight and climb aboard. Buckey's nostrils flared, his eyes gleamed, and we'd be off, bucking, snorting, and backfiring. It usually took a mile or so to get the vinegar out of him, and then he'd be steady for the rest of the day.

As we made our way along, we checked the salt blocks, the water holes, and mended fence here and there. The sun was bright, and all creation was glad to be alive. Bill broke into a toothless grin when we located some cattle roaming free. We rounded them up and drove them to the midway cabin.

This was an old homestead a miner had occupied in years gone by. He had left a note on the door which read: "Twelve miles to water, seven miles to wood, three inches to hell, heading west to heaven!"

It was a rough but, still, a good place to spend the night. We dusted things off, killed a few rattlesnakes that had taken up residence, and Bill began to cook supper. He always started meals the same way—with a dirty coffeepot. He would add a pound of coffee beans, wet it down with some mosquito infested water, and then boil it over the fire for a half hour.

To test the coffee's readiness, he'd throw an old horseshoe in the pot. If it sank, he'd add more coffee.

We weren't too hungry. We ate so much dirt riding tail on that bunch of cattle that our stomachs were full. It always happened. We got so good we could tell what section of the ranch we were on blindfolded, just by tasting the dirt.

Bill finished the meal of meat and biscuits and set it down. I broke open a biscuit, took a bite, and commented, "It's burned on the outside, raw in the middle, and salty as a salt block. Just the way I like 'em!"

I couldn't say anything bad. Only a buzzard would pick on his friends. Besides, I couldn't cook. And ranch rules said that if you ever complained about the food, you had to do the cooking.

The next morning, we continued our ride in silence until Bill suddenly reined up. In his strained voice, he said, "I'm gonna show you my best-kept secret." Then he turned his horse north, and we rode for another hour through thick pine forests. At the top of a long wooded ridge, we dismounted and walked to a large outcropping of rock. Peering over the edge, my eyes beheld the most beautiful view I ever saw. A huge valley meadow stretched below. Lush vegetation grew in living green, watered by a clear-flowing stream that wound its way down. The spectacular rocky mountains formed a magnificent backdrop, reflecting the bright afternoon sun.

"We'll jes sit here an wait," Bill said, and with that, he lay down, covered his face with his old Stetson, and was soon snoring. I didn't know what we were waiting for, but I also knew better than to ask. As the evening chill began to settle in the valley, Bill woke up. After a few coughs and complaints about his old bones, he collected himself and peered over the ridge. "Ha!" he hoarsely whispered, "there they is, just as I knowed they'd be!"

Below us now was a huge herd of elk, or "wapiti," the Indian name Bill called them. There were several bulls,and many cow elk grazing contentedly, while a number of playful calves jumped about.

"I done come here purt near every year since long before you was born. Right from this here rock I hunted an I ain't never seen hide ner hair of no one else. Ain't nobody knows about this place. Jist you an me." Bill put his rough hand on my shoulder and continued. "I'm gettin' too old to come here now—can't pack the meat out anyhow. So, I'm givin' it all to you, son. Take good care of it. An' don't you rat on me to no city slickers 'bout this spot. They'll want to turn it into a newfangled resort or somethin'."

We shook hands. There was a gleam in the old man's eyes. Although I couldn't fully realize why, I knew Bill had entrusted to me one of the most personal possessions of his heart.

Bill was pushing dandelions just a few years later. Only once did I return to the valley. It was still there untouched. I've not been back for eighteen years now. Nor have I ever shown anyone the old man's secret. That's the way Bill wanted it. His grave site is lonely, but now Bill's asleep where he wanted. His tombstone was never written, but if I could have chosen a verse, it would have been this:

When life is over and my race is run,
When death shadows gather and my time has come,

Leo Schreven

When I've rode my last horse and have turned my last steer,
When my spirit's winged its way to that celestial sphere,
When my grave has been dug and I've been laid to rest,
Please let it be in the far, far West.*
J. E. McCauley

Bill and I had shared many good times. One hilarious event took place in the fall roundup. We were branding a bunch of calves in the stock pens. This was a grand time of dust, dirt, burning hair, and sweat.

Poor Oma would greet me at the door for supper wearing a gas mask and make me take off my savory clothes and boots outside. This was embarrassing, since my physique wasn't exactly Herculean. Even the dog would blink and run behind the barn with his tail between his legs. But the embarrassment was worth the fun of the day. My bath water would drain into the river in front of the house, and that probably explains why I could only catch trout upstream.

At any rate, on that fine day we went in search of stray calves, and about noon I spotted one in a gulch. Buckey's ears perked, and we were off chasing the little critter.

Now folks, I've met some bad calves over the years, but this little fellow was worse than ten miles of bad road. After chasing him for three hours, I still couldn't get near enough to rope him. He was quick and knew every trick in the book—and had added a few chapters besides. Finally, we were able to run him out of the canyon and onto a mile-long mesa. Buckey raced toward the fleeing calf, and I was finally able to take a real shot at roping it. But that goofy calf had some strange built-in springs in his legs and jumped the noose at the same time I jerked back. The noose tightened around his right back leg as Buckey reared to a halt.

While the calf kept running, I quickly wrapped the rope around

---

*Cowboy Wisdom Roundup by Terry Hall with Greg Stebben. Copyright 1995 by Modern Man Books. All Rights Reserved. Published by Warner Books Inc. N.Y.

the saddle horn. It was satisfying to see the calf hit the end and come to a screeching halt, pulling at least seven Gs. Buckey stood his ground while I ran down the rope to the fighting calf.

Now, a calf that's roped proper around the neck poses no problem. They usually back up against the rope while you throw them. This is simply accomplished by grabbing the left foreleg with the left hand and the right back leg by the right hand. A quick jerk and the calf is on its back. You then slip the noose around the neck and foreleg, and then lead the calf back to the stock pen.

But this situation was unique because the calf was running all over, caught only by one leg! After being dragged around for a while through cactus and sage, I was finally able to grab the proper legs and jerk. However, I forgot about those strange springs built into this goofy calf, and as I jerked, it jumped!

Now to most folks, lying under two hundred pounds of beef might not be intimidating, but to a scrawny fourteen-year-old kid, it brought back visions of making more Band-Aid commercials. I still remember the impact for three reasons:

One—the weight of the calf fell on my chest, knocking the wind out of me. I was gasping like a fish out of water.

Two—I was on my back in a lovely bed of prickly-pear cactus (this is where the Band-Aid commercials came in).

Three—when I caught my breath again, I wished I hadn't. There was a dreadfully strange odor about. About three inches from my nose, I saw why. Gazing down at my now ragged T-shirt and jeans, I could see that the old saying was true for calves as well as people—"when Mother Nature calls, you gotta go!"

That's exactly what the calf had done. Right on me.

I don't reckon there was a more miserable kid in Colorado that day. Even Buckey turned up his nose at me. With my britches full of cactus, my clothes covered with fresh cow pies, and my pride dragging in the dust behind me, I painfully made my way to the river and there took a long swim. All the fish downstream temporarily moved to new homes upstream as I washed my britches and Bill picked out my cactus friends who had tagged along.

Meanwhile, the ranch manager had secured the calf and brought it to me. If I had given the manager the same look as I gave the calf, I reckon the manager would have been stunned, if not killed outright!

You can understand then why I asked the ranch manager if I could be the one to brand this particular calf?

He grinned and gave his OK. It wasn't exactly the prettiest brand I've ever seen. In fact, it took several attempts to get it right.

Finally, the manager, unable to contain his laughter any longer, decreed that the calf was branded.

The calf and I both healed quickly. Visiting folk who saw the calf often asked why it had a dozen brands and the others had only one? The calf and I would eyeball each other, and I'd mumble something about some cows getting special treatment.

The ranch manager also owned one of the finest quarterhorse mares on the range. She was solid chestnut with a white blaze down her face and one white sock. She was bred to a fine stallion and was to foal in the spring. I took a special interest in the mare and the manager noticed. We made a deal that if I liked her foal, I could work for it and buy it.

The occasion arrived early one morning. In the sweet grass of our back meadow, little Starlight was born. I named him after another horse I had read about. Starlight was perfect. He stood on his wobbly legs as the mare stood by his side. He grew quickly and was full of life and mischief, as all little foals are. I dreamed often of the wonderful years we would spend together. I began to train him early, and he showed much promise. Starlight was every cowboy's dream come true.

As school started that fall, Starlight was four months old. One afternoon, an exceptionally severe thunderstorm passed through, with high wind and hail. Leaving school, I was anxious to get home to see Starlight, and I went immediately to the front pasture. The mare was there with her nose down nuzzling Starlight. At first glance, all seemed well.

Then I noticed Starlight's face. It was covered with blood. Blood flowed from his nostrils and mouth. My heart stopped. A brief look around told the story. Starlight had been frightened by the storm and had panicked. Running on the wet grass, he slipped and hit the barbwire fence. The barbs had cut deep gashes into his face and nostrils. Starlight couldn't move.

We quickly called the vet. He and the ranch manager carefully picked up Starlight and moved him into the warm barn, where I made a bed of clean dry straw. The vet worked on him for several hours. I stroked Starlight's back and fought a deep gnawing pain that was growing in my stomach.

When the vet spoke, my heart sank. "It's bad, son. Starlight has swallowed a lot of blood, and his lungs are full. There are many complications–I don't think he'll make it."

I felt tears burning in my eyes, and a huge lump in my throat wouldn't let me speak. The manager put his hand on my shoulder, "Come on, son. It will be easier this way."

I shook my head, still unable to speak. I couldn't leave Starlight. They left me alone there. I wept and prayed. "Please, God, don't let him die," I pleaded. My heart ached more than words could express.

Starlight's breathing became more labored. The inability to do anything to relieve his suffering tore my heart apart. I held his head on my lap, teardrops dampening his beautiful brown coat. Starlight died there. His final choking breath faded, and a quiet peace filled the barn. I laid Starlight's head down gently on the warm straw and kissed his forehead. Stepping out into the cool night air, I gazed up at the millions of stars, a void as big as the universe in my heart. *Why God? Why?*

The next morning was a church day. Opa dropped off the rest of the family, but he took me on a drive to the Buckhorn canyon. This was a favorite wilderness area we often drove through. He spoke to me there of life and of being strong. He was understanding. I did not understand all his words at the time, but his kindness to me at that moment was comforting.

In my heart, I was angry at God for letting this happen. This was the third time in my life I had to give up a beloved horse. Why wouldn't God let me have something I could keep? Why did He always take it from me?

Dad just encouraged me to trust God. If we could see the end from the beginning, we would understand. He helped me accept that and to have confidence in God, knowing that all things work together for good.

That was twenty years ago. I still miss Starlight, but today I can begin to understand. God's ultimate plan for my life and happiness involved more than temporary things. He foresaw that my greatest joy would be in traveling around the world sharing His love with others. This would be impossible if I were still a cowboy tied down to a ranch, horses, and cattle.

So from an early age, He disciplined me to not be attached to earthly things. As I look back now, I'm glad for those lessons. And besides, in a few years when the Lord comes and we all go to that big roundup in the sky, I plan to have a good horse throughout eternity.

A lot of times, things in life don't turn out as we planned. Sometimes life isn't fair. We get hurt by people. Some are abused in different ways. We can become victims of things beyond our control. And the eternal question remains: "Why, God?"

I still have some of those questions unanswered, and that's OK, because I also have an inner peace. God loves us. He has a lot more wisdom than we do. And since He knows the end from the beginning, it's good to relax, knowing you're in the hands of a great God and a loving heavenly Father.

Some things we'll eventually understand while we're here on earth. But on other things, we'll have to wait and talk it over in the by and by. So, trust in God. Stay close to Him through daily devotion, Bible study, and prayer. He is your best friend. And soon, when He comes, we'll look back at this life, and, compared to the delights and joys of heaven, we won't even remember why we asked, "Why?"

Don't miss it for anything.

They say there will be a great roundup,
And cowboys, like dogies, will stand,

COWBOYS MAKE BETTER PREACHERS

To be mavericked by the Riders of Judgment
Who are posted and know every brand.
I know there's many a stray cowboy
Who'll be last in at the great final sale,
When he might have gone to green pastures
Had he known the dim narrow trail.

I wonder if ever a cowboy
Stood ready for that Judgment Day
And could say to the Boss of the Riders,
"I'm ready, come drive me away."

They say He will never forget you,
That He knows ever action and look;
So, for safety, you'd better get branded,
Have your name in His big Tally Book,

To be shipped to that bright mystic region,
Over there in green pastures to lie,
And be led by the crystal still waters
To the home in the sweet by-and-by.

The road to that far happy region
Is a dim narrow trail, so they say;
But the bright one that leads to perdition
Is posted and blazed all the way.
–Traditional

150
100
50
0

CHAPTER

School Daze

A young cowboy always dreams of going to school to learn the three Rs—Roping, Riding, and Rodeo. You can only imagine my utter disappointment when, after my first week in school, I hadn't even seen a horse or saddle! This disappointment was compounded further when my classmate Billy happily informed me that Elmer's glue was made from horsehoofs! This led to my first suspension from school at age six, after Billy mysteriously lost his front teeth.

Mrs. McGuimus, my first-grade teacher, was a saint if there ever was one. She informed Oma and Opa that they were parents of a hyperactive six-year-old child who couldn't sit still, shut up, or pay attention. Her advice was to let me play in class all year, and at age seven—hopefully having matured—I would be sentenced to first grade to start my proper education.

School was always a bittersweet event. I loved to learn but was always restless when cooped up in a room with four walls. Recess was my favorite class, and I got straight As in it from grades one to twelve.

COWBOYS MAKE BETTER PREACHERS

It was in first grade (the second time) that I discovered my body was wired at 220 volts while most children ran 110. I felt sorry for them but didn't hold it against them. I even went out of my way to treat the others as normal. There was, however, one particularly zesty day when my voltage regulator went on the blink, and I burned out.

It happened while we were all playing "pom-pom-pullaway" (This was before P.E., baseball, and normal recess activities). The game consisted of children holding one rope on the ground and extending another one farther and farther. You had to jump across the ropes without touching them. As the ropes grew farther and farther apart, you had to jump longer and longer, usually landing on your rear end so your feet would clear the rope. It ate the bottom out of several of my britches and usually didn't stop there, but Mom always managed to find a patch.

On this fateful day, while making a run, I just gave out. Everything went black, and I woke up with the teacher cradling me in her arms on the sidewalk. It was terribly embarrassing, but she eventually got over it.

When I regained my senses, I tried to walk but could only go a few feet before sitting down, totally exhausted. I found that if I waited five minutes, I could go again for another three minutes before blacking out again. After a few weeks of this, we went to see a doctor.

He informed Oma that I was totally burned out at age seven. His prescription to cure this was worse than imaginable—"Multiple vitamins, extra iron tablets, and *two hours of sleep* each afternoon after school." I protested loudly enough that they called the ambulance to the rescue. Unfortunately, the doctor survived, with the use of a hearing aid.

It was worse than eating zucchini. Here I was in first grade, sentenced to taking naps in my sister's room two hours each afternoon while my brothers and friends played outside. My outrage and frustration was usually taken out on Raggedy Ann and Raggedy Andy. These were two large dolls Oma had made for my sister. Within two weeks, the stuffing was floating around the house from poor Raggedy Andy. Oma resewed him together so many times that by fourth grade he was the only doll ever held together with over a million stitches.

For the next three years, I endured this medieval torture and by fourth grade, my body was strong again, and I was beginning to really enjoy school. My teacher that year was Mrs. Pflugrad. She was a fantastic teacher. After two weeks of English, she called me to the front of the class, threw up her hands, and said that my papers were full of the most exaggerated, farfetched, and questionable ideas any rational mind (meaning hers) had ever read! My spelling, speech, and cynical attitude approached complete illiteracy! I felt completely embarrassed, not being used to such compliments, especially in front of the whole class!

"I'm going to make you literate if it takes the rest of your life!" Mrs. Pflugrad said. What "It" was that I was supposed to litter I wasn't sure, but I was too smart to let her know.

Mrs. Pflugrad continued her treatise. "Fifteen percent of school children are below normal mentally, and if you don't get educated quickly, you'll join them!" I told her, that fifteen percent had to be too high a figure, since we don't have that many people working in the government. I could tell she was impressed, because she remained speechless.

That day was a turning point in school for me. Mrs. Pflugrad took me aside, told me if I thought education was difficult, to try ignorance. She then took a personal interest in me. She introduced me to the world of reading. It sounds simple enough, but she opened up a whole new dimension of life.

It began with cash prizes each Friday to whomever read the most that week. She gave me a book called *Little House in the Big Woods* by Laura Ingalls Wilder. She challenged me to read it all that week and win the one-dollar prize. I did it. And I won! I was hooked on reading! Suddenly, I could become a part of anyone's world: Hunting bears in the big woods of Wisconsin with Mr. Ingalls. Stalking Indians with Daniel Boone. Fishing in the Mississippi with Huckleberry

Finn, or cowboying with Ben K. Green.

Then something even more amazing happened! I suddenly knew more than anyone in class. When the teacher had a question, I frequently had the answer.

"How did you know that?" she would ask in astonishment, her eyes growing misty.

"I read it," I'd reply.

It was the beginning of a love affair that's never ended. To think, in a few hours, you can digest a book that took a person a *lifetime* of study and experience to put together! Amazing! You can read one book on any topic; sports, automobiles, health, family, religion, finance, etc., and be knowledgeable for the rest of your life in that area!

Reading changed my life. I highly recommend it. TV has destroyed a lot of reading time, but most TV is for deadheads and zombies. You are just a sieve with stuff floating in and out. Try reading at least one good book a week. It will be one of the best decisions you will ever make, especially if the book says "Pacific Press" on it.

Mrs. Pflugrad also got me involved in music and encouraged me to learn the trumpet and saxophone, something my dog never forgave her for. For the dog's sake, I finally traded the sax off for a good cow. It made about the same noise and gave milk besides. We lived happily ever after.

As my formal education progressed to seventh and eighth grade, I had the unfortunate pleasure of being taught by Chuck. I enjoyed sitting at the feet of this teacher, although having your desk upwind was preferable. Our country school lacked accredited teachers, and Chuck was a volunteer. He was a strange mixture of mountain man and logger, with a lot of brains and no teaching ability whatsoever.

Chuck loved to camp, and one of our earliest classes was on wilderness survival. I'm not sure what particular university recommended such a course for eighth grade, but out on the range such trifling matters didn't matter much.

We began our wilderness quest hiking up Buckhorn Canyon, heading for a creek that was thirteen miles away. Chuck taught us how to read a map, and by three o'clock that afternoon, we were hopelessly lost. A slow panic seized us as the cold Colorado night began to creep upon us. Recognizing our imminent need to be rescued, I finally resorted to the time-proven emergency-distress signal—three shots fired in rapid succession. The light was so bad, however, that I missed Chuck, and we were still lost.

"No problem," Chuck said, "Just watch and learn how to survive!" Chuck prided himself on his knowledge of wild edible foods and proceeded to tell us that even if we were lost, we would never starve. He suddenly stooped down and picked some leaves off a plant.

"Ever eat any water crescent?" he asked authoritatively, handing us all some. We all chewed a few leaves.

"Well, this ain't it," Chuck said after a few moments. "You all don't never want to eat any plant that ever looks like this!" We all dug in our packs for Pepto-Bismol and survived with the use of CPR.

After climbing over hundreds of logs, battling brush, slogging through swamps, and tunneling through clouds of mosquitos, we finally stumbled onto the creek. It was a beautiful sight—large boulders, soft sand, trees lining its sides. The only problem was that the creek had no water.

The only academic lessons I recall having on this trip were in language. Our vocabulary increased substantially as we learned new adjectives to describe our feelings. Chuck gave us each an "A plus."

After eking through elementary school and being kicked out several times, my parents sent me to a school in another state in vain hopes of it being able to "straighten me out." The reform school was tough. We guys could not talk to girls. The food was all vegetarian. Worst of all, they cut off all your hair! Believe me, this was a traumatic experience for all teenagers of the seventies. We worked all day on a farm in desert heat—picking peas, shelling peas, and hoeing peas. Sometimes there was more variety—changing water lines, picking corn, tomatoes, or melons.

Nights were spent peeling skin from each other's ears. It was pitiful to see your buddy's beautiful ears, once covered with long, flowing hair, now naked and bare to the desert sun, cracking and peeling. We *looked* like little devils; no wonder we acted like them!

The only relief to the desert heat on the whole campus was two ponds that offered a chance for swimming each afternoon. It was here I first struck gold. Racing my buddy Jim to the pond one afternoon, I arrived just in time to see a huge bass spook near the shore. Jim arrived and quickly spotted another one. Understand now, Jim and I were hungry for some real meat. The vegetarian diet of beans and peas had left us craving some soul food—the type that tries to crawl off your plate before you get to it. And so together we cooked up a plan.

As the sun set that day, Jim and I sneaked out of our cabin. Quietly, we made our way to the pond. We tied a lure onto a piece of old fishing line. Without the benefit of a pole, we cast the lure out. Slowly we retrieved it back, its plastic body wiggling across the calm surface.

From out of nowhere, a huge bass came like a missile from the depths and detonated on our lure. A few minutes later, Mr. Bass was in two neat filets in our cabin. Our excitement could hardly be contained!

"Wow, man, I can't wait to eat it." Jim said.

"Yea, where can we fry it?" I replied.

We looked at each other in disbelief. Where could we fry it? We thought of every plan possible, with no solution. Desperate men, however, find desperate solutions. We eyeballed the wood stove in the cabin. The thermometer on the wall read 92 degrees.

"If we build a fire in the wood stove to fry these filets, we're going to have a foretaste of Revelation 20:9," Jim said.

"Yea, but if you don't build one we're going to have the continued taste of peas and beans." I reminded him.

"Light it!" Jim laughed as he spoke.

And so we gathered together all the trash in the room (which proved to be the equivalent of several pickup loads), and lit the wood stove. In no time, the stove was hot. We poured a little cooking oil we had borrowed on top. It sizzled nicely as we laid the filets carefully down.

By now the thermometer had reached 130 degrees, and we had to open the cabin door to even breathe. The floor was awash with sweat, and the aroma of frying fish filled the night air.

"What on earth are you guys doing in there?" The bewildered voice caught us by surprise. We looked out to see Mr. Scobie, the dreaded music teacher who also passed for boys' dean, walking toward our cabin. His eyes were stern and his nose twitched suspiciously.

"We're just burning trash, Mr. Scobie," Jim yelled.

"At ten o'clock in the evening? In the middle of August? Why don't you just put it in bags and dump it like normal teenagers? And what's that fishy smell?"

"Fishy smell? I don't smell nothing fishy. Do you, Leo?" Jim yelled again.

"Must be my old pair of socks, Mr. Scobie. Now don't you worry, we'll be done burning shortly, and we'll get some rest." I was on my way out of the cabin to intercept Mr. Scobie. "Say, by the way, I was going to ask you to let me sing tenor in the choir this year. What do you think?" Mr. Scobie's face brightened up as we turned and walked slowly away.

"I had no idea that you were interested in music and singing, Leo. Why, sure, I would love to hear you sing tenor!" He shook my hand and walked away.

I smiled and looked to the distant mountains. I'd love to sing tenor—ten or eleven miles away from anybody!

Back at the cabin, the fish filets were bubbling and popping. We drooled and sniffed the savory aroma. I rounded up a couple of plates, and we carried the flavorful fish out to the melon patch. The desert night air cooled our sweating bodies as we savored each bite. We found the biggest, heaviest melon in the patch and split it with an ax. I ate half, and Jim ate the other half. Looking back, it was one of the nicest feasts I've ever enjoyed.

Unfortunately, this was our only feast, as my high school career was cut short a few days later—only six weeks after arrival.

After church one beautiful day, the boys and I were restless and needed to blow off a little steam. After much begging, we got the principal to take us up to the mountains in his van. En route, we stopped to look at something, and I spotted four old tires someone had dumped on the side of the road. While the principal was preaching about the amazing wonders of creation, I sneaked the tires into the back of the van.

As the drive continued, Jim and I created a plan. At the top of the mountain, with the beautiful valley laying thirteen miles below, the principal began another one of his lectures on nature. We sneaked out the tires and rolled them to the edge of the mountain. With a great war hoop, we sent two tires flying down.

It was an awesome sight. The tires gained momentum in excess of 140 mph. The police officer who was running radar verified this later and was scratching his head trying to figure out why at 140 mph he could see the tires but not the car?

As the tires sped down the mountain, rabbits dove for cover, deer got a severe case of diarrhea, and rattlesnakes simply got squashed. Then the tires hit rocks and bounced right into orbit–the space shuttle crew reported two UFO's. We were all whooping and yelling at the top of our lungs.

"Stop it!" The principal was red in the face. "Stop what you're doing!" I wanted to point out that this was near impossible. But before I could say so, he grabbed me and gave me a tongue-lashing about profaning the Lord's day and how I was going to hell for being such a sinner. Not being converted at that point, I told him if heaven was full of red-faced, yelling weirdos like him, I didn't figure on being there anyway.

"Get in the van right now!" he roared.

I obeyed grudgingly. However, on the way, I accidentally stumbled over the other two tires, and, unbelievably, they went over the bank like the first two. I tried to explain this to the principal, but at this point, his facial expression was the sort of thing a fourteen-year-old boy should never be allowed to see. For years to come, it would cause me to wake up whimpering in the night.

It wasn't until the next day that I realized how seriously I had ticked him off. Returning to the dorm after a thrilling day of hoeing peas, I was greeted by my oma and opa.

"Where did you come from?" I gasped.

Oma had tears in her eyes, and Opa looked solemn. His lips tightened as he spoke. "Didn't they tell you why we're here?"

By now it was clear to me someone must have died in the family or something else disastrous had occurred. I anxiously asked who died or what happened. Oma and Opa looked at each other.

"Are you sure no one told you why we're here?" Opa demanded.

"No," I answered. "Please tell me!"

"We got a phone call last night and drove all night and day to come pick up our rebellious son!"

"You mean no one's dead? I'm the reason you're here?" I was stunned.

The discovery of such a foreboding thought filled me with apprehension. It's a good thing psychology and political correctness had not yet been invented, or I would have been emotionally scarred for life by these events.

It was a lonely ride home. Here I was, at age fourteen, kicked out of school again. My parents were ready to give up on me, the school hated me, and I was sure God hated me–if there was a God. Life was so low I could scratch my navel with my backbone.

You would think that it couldn't get worse. Wrong.

After arriving home, there was no school that would take me, so I decided to just stay on the ranch and work with horses. I was forced to go to church, although I hated every minute of it. The only bright spot in church was a darling little filly named Desiree, my puppy-love sweetheart. One look at her was worth the entire sermon. One look is usually all I got, too, since everyone was busy trying to keep her as far away from me as possible.

It so happened not long after my arrival at home that there were two church leaders who especially despised me. These were real Quaker-type men who prided themselves in eating only two meals a day, never mixing their fruits and vegetables, and eating no milk, eggs, or cheese. They had a profound knowledge of an author named

Ellen G. White and delivered sermons that a turtle could have kept up with. Every time I went within twenty feet of them, I felt like a nervous wreck. They missed their vocation—a monastery in Italy would have been perfect.

One of these men had caught Desiree and I smiling and winking at each other during one of his boring sermons. Strange things began to form in his little brain, and before long, he reported to my parents that I was having an affair with Desiree. Now remember, folks, I was only fourteen. I didn't even know what an "affair" was. I had never even touched Desiree, except a little kiss, but the preacher must have been convincing, because when I got home Opa was fuming. No, he was smoking. Really, he was raging!

I'll never forget that moment. Opa roared something about making complete rearrangement of my anatomy once he got hold of it, and the whooping began. Belts and words were flying all over as we wove a verbal tapestry brilliant in color and blinding in intensity. Opa's was a bit too imaginative to write down; mine was more general! *OOOOAAAGHHHA WAGHYEEEEE!!!*

When it was over, I stumbled out of the house looking like a creature put together by a drunk taxidermist. My anger knew no limits, and I vowed never to return home. I also vowed to terminate the preacher who lied and caused all this. I vowed to burn down his church. In general, I was headed for disaster.

God looked down from heaven at that moment. And in a last ditch effort to save me, He arranged to hit me upside the head with a two-by-four and wake me up. Since I'm still recovering 18 years later and can't remember all the important details, I've given my brother Squirrel the incredible opportunity to write the next chapter and explain it all.

CHAPTER

God, Guns, and Outlaws

Herman Schreven

Chuck Yeager punching through the sound barrier; Benjamin Franklin's wife telling him to go fly a kite in an electric storm; Fred Flintstone's invention of the wheel; Albert Einstein's development of nuclear energy—all these events changed the world. The story I am about to relate is also one that changed the world.

OK, maybe only Leo's world—maybe not. The story is true. None of the names have been changed to protect the identity of the innocent or guilty. Leo seems to have been so traumatized by this event that he is unable to get his facts straight. To his credit, he had the smarts to ask someone of superior intelligence to write this chapter.

Allow me to introduce myself. I am Leo's youngest brother. The one frequently referred to in this book as "Squirrel." With a real name of Herman, Squirrel didn't seem too bad, so the name stuck.

Back when my parents decided to be real Christians, they made one fateful decision. Being on fire like most born-again people, they actually believed the Bible when it said, "Flee to the mountains!" They promptly sold our house in the evil city and next thing Leo and I knew, we were gasping on thin mountain air. Seven-thousand feet above sea level in the Colorado Rockies, to be exact. They moved us so far from civilization that satellite TV couldn't even reach us! I left home to go to boarding academy when I was six years old and got to the school just in time to begin my freshman year at the age of fourteen.

This story begins three days before Christmas in 1976. That year we had a visit. Nope, it wasn't a ghost of past, present, or future. It was two gentlemen bearing not gifts, but shotguns. So much for leaving the evils of the big city. Much to our horror, the evils came to us! There are some things in life you just never can get far enough away from–like brussel sprouts or zucchini, for instance.

We were sitting around a warm, crackling fireplace (they couldn't find enough wire to get electricity to our place) when these two miserable crooks walked in. Being away from the wicked city, there was no need to lock any doors, so these low life's just came in without even knocking. They immediately put enough distance between our family and themselves to give the buckshot in their guns maximum efficiency. The distance also kept us from grabbing them and doing things we may have had to repent for in church the next day. Before we had time to say one word, they screamed at us, "Shut up and do as you're told, and nobody will get hurt!"

We immediately got off to a bad start. You see, my oldest brother, John, had flown in from out of state just two hours before. His girlfriend, whom I will call Mary because that really was her name, came with him. While the rest of us sat in stunned terror, Mary was emitting an annoying laugh.

Hehehe . . . ugghee, heee, agggah, hehe . . .

We understood why when she snuggled up to John and said that the whole scene was a sick joke and she wanted to know who these friends of his were. She actually believed that John had set the whole thing up. That was ridiculous! We had lived on that mountain for three years, and not one of our friends had ever found our house, in spite of great direction-giving.

While Mary kept laughing, some of us started praying.

My oma had the best direct line to heaven most of the time, but especially that night. Most of us in that room were too busy pleading for forgiveness to even bother asking for deliverance. At first Oma started silently, but within moments, she was praying out loud. The senior gunman went into a tirade and with many colorful (mostly blue) expletives told her, "Shut up, or I will blow your head off."

Everything was working backward. First, we moved into the country to get away from the evils of city life. That idea got blown to smithereens. Then my dear mother started praying, and our persecutors went completely psycho. I want you to understand one thing. I had been to 624 church services in my short life. Twelve years old times fifty-two weeks. I had heard 624 stories of missionaries who were about to become "what's for dinner" when suddenly they prayed and the spears of the heathen savages became like angel-hair pasta after ten minutes in boiling water.

It didn't take long for me to figure out that to all human observations, God had a different set of rules for His chosen in North America. My dear and inspired Oma finally stopped praying out loud. The irritated gunmen were relieved. As ashamed as I am to admit it, so was I.

The two hoodlums quickly figured out a system for pillaging our modest house. One would stand at his post of duty while the other searched the house for treasures we had laid up on earth. It wasn't much. We were "poah," as they say in the South.

The "post" at which they did their tour of duty was a breakfast bar that jutted out from the wall and separated the kitchen from the dining room. As they stood behind that counter, they pulled an arsenal of shells out of their pockets and neatly lined them up on the counter. I thought it was a rather crude way to establish their own self-worth, but they seemed delighted.

The counter, which they thought was a trench, was about twenty feet from where our family was seated around the fireplace. There was nothing in between the end of the gun's barrel and us, except thin mountain air. One good blast of buckshot out of the double barrel, and our family would be fast-forwarded into eternity. Which eternity I am not certain. By the look on Leo's face and the thoughts ricocheting around in my head, I had a feeling it would be a real warm eternity! Mary was laughing less frequently and beginning to get impatient with John. What's a guy to do?

After these rascals had spent some time rooting around, they decided they could save time trying to find our hidden treasure by jamming one of the guns in my opa's back and just asking him where it was. The one gun-wielding coward stayed back to guard the family while the other came, stood Opa up, put the gun in his back, and told him to boot it into the back bedroom.

If things had seemed bad, they just got worse. It was kind of like flying across the prairie in a twin-engine plane with one engine dead and then having the second engine catch on fire after you are deep into the Rocky Mountains. You know it's just a matter of time before you "buy the farm." I knew for certain that they were going to kill my dad in the bedroom and then kill us off one at a time by making us eat zucchini and brussel sprouts until we exploded.

There was silence in the Schreven home for the space of about ten minutes. Then the bedroom door was opened, and out came a being who had the appearance of a man, but his face was as white as the wind-driven snow, and his steps were as those of a wino. Almost sounds apocalyptic, doesn't it?

My opa lived through World War II in Holland. He served as an MP on the Dutch/German border. He raised three normal children, plus Leo, and faced other equally terrifying events in his life, so he was not one to scare easily. I watched him stagger to where we were seated and crumble into his chair. He was shaking so violently I am certain they felt it in California and thought the "big one" was about to hit. Oma, sensing her wifely duty, leaned over to ask him what was wrong.

The senior thug saw her and shouted, "Don't ask, lady."

Things were dragging on a bit too long, and Oma decided it was time to pray again. Just for double measure, you understand. If we thought we were getting edgy, we quickly discovered our terrorists were as edgy as a fool playing roulette with five live bullets and one blank. The previous tirade, multiplied ten times, was heaped upon my mother and everyone else within five miles, which included only our family and the local coyotes. Oma finally stopped praying. Whew!

Unfortunately, it was only long enough for her to take a shallow breath and begin singing. I recall that the selection she chose for the occasion was "Praise God From Whom All Blessings Flow." Schreven historians are unable to agree on which song it was, but there is a strong consensus that it was horribly inappropriate. The gunmen continued to hurl threats at Oma, accompanied with wild gun gyrations for several long minutes. Oma finally stopped. At long last, they simmered down to a hard, rolling boil.

All present took a deep breath and let out a collective "Wowee, that was close!" sigh. The hoodlums mumbled to each other for a while then took turns pillaging the house while the other kept the gun pointed at us from the safety of the kitchen counter. Having completed their search for valuable stuff and only coming up with twenty dollars and Leo's cheap guitar, they decided it was time to resume their own miniature version of the Gestapo again. The oldest thug marched over to Opa and went through the gun-in-the-back sequence again. Moments later, I heard the door of the back bedroom slam shut and knew once again that these evil men were going to end my father's life.

I must interject a bit of seriousness here. Not because it is my nature to do so, but because I think a point needs to be made, and I can't find a humorous way to do it. I was a typical twelve-year-old kid who was just starting into the teenage stage. I thought my parents were strange, out of touch, and made way too many rules. I would have left home if I thought I would have had a chance of making it. When I saw Opa being marched into the bedroom and heard the door close, I suddenly realized that my opa was pretty special, and the most important person in my life. He was someone I knew I did not want to lose or go through the rest of my life without. If you are a teenager reading this story, put the book down and go give your opa a hug or a punch or whatever gesture you use to express affection and appreciation. If you are the parent of a teenager and are feeling that your kids don't love or respect you, well, trust me—they do. In time, they will get around to letting you know.

I had ceased pleading for my own life and decided it might be more worth my time to pray for someone who really deserved and needed it. Someone like Leo, but I opted to start praying for my dad. OK, so I did have some ulterior motives, like, "Who will pay me allowance?" and that sort of thing.

While Opa was being interrogated by Hitler's grandson twice removed on his mother's aunt's side, I had plenty of time to think about my own short life up to that point in time. I was glad this was happening while I was young, because I had too much to think about as it was. I would have gone stir crazy trying to confess everything if this had happened when I was fifty! The sure way to avoid a situation like this is to live right to start with, and if you do slip up, make sure you make peace with God the day it happens.

The door finally opened, and it was like apocalypse all over again. My opa was so white, he would have made Casper the friendly ghost look like an African American. Knees rattled, and the house shook as Dad made his way over to join his family. Oma took one look, and guess what she did? Another medley of singing, praying, and quoting Bible promises. To make things really interesting, she even sang some of the Bible verses and prayed a few hymns.

The display of displeasure from our visitors would have made the Fourth of July celebration in Washington, D.C. look like a single sparkler. I knew Oma was going to be the first one to get shot, and they would no doubt go on to shoot the rest of us, just because we were related to her. It was about then the Lord looked down and decided it was time to teach the young Schreven kids a lesson, especially Leo, since he was easily the worst of the bunch. In fact, as I look back, we could have avoided all this if God hadn't had to slap Leo upside the head and straighten him out.

As the gunman put his shotgun in Oma's face, my dear mother looked straight down the barrel of that gun, right into the eyes of that devil-possessed kid and kept right on singing and praying! There was no stopping or backing down this time. No sooner had she done this than the guy started to calm down. It was not instantly, but after a few minutes, his rage had subsided into a very disgruntled mumble. I was impressed.

I was just beginning to feel like things were going to be all right, when my thoughts were interrupted by the barking of our assailants. “Get into the woodshed now, all of you!” My dad politely told them that we did not have a woodshed! It was the truth but not the response they wanted to hear.

“Don’t lie to me, or I will kill you all here and now,” the gunman screamed back.

A quick surveillance mission by his partner proved that we were indeed telling the truth.

“OK, then, get in the garage,” came the quick command.

The garage was not the greatest place, but it did seem a nicer place than getting killed in the woodshed. We rose to our feet and formed a single line with about five feet between each of us. I was the last in line as we trudged fearfully into the garage. Being in the back of the line, it was my turn to get the gun in my back. It should have been Leo. He had already committed more sin in fifteen years than most folk do in a lifetime.

Oma was the first one in the garage. She observed that the back door was open and decided to make a run for it. This was a brilliant idea but one she probably had not prayed about. She got halfway down the driveway before the thought occurred to her that they just might kill all of us when they did their roll call and discovered she was missing.

She did a quick 180-degree turn, came back, and peaked in the window to see how her family was doing. We were not doing well. She rushed in and joined the rest of us as we stood with our backs to the wall and shotguns in our faces. The would-be bandits were shocked and confused to realize what had happened, so they accepted her explanation that the dog had gotten out and she just went to get it!

Amazing! If intelligence were crankcase oil, those guys wouldn't even wet the dipstick.

By now, it was obvious to all of us that these delinquents had seen way too much TV and had a real bent for violence. In case you have been wondering if Mary was still laughing away in denial, I can assure you she quit when we were in the garage. She may actually have come to grips with reality sooner, but in the garage I remember noticing that she seemed to have figured out these guys were not our friends. Please don't misunderstand me. Mary is not a dense person. She is quite bright. She was just dating a guy who belonged to a family that displayed a strange sense of humor from time to time.

The bad guys had us empty all our pockets onto the garage floor. All the cash and currency combined came to a stunning total of $21.85. An average contribution of $3.12 per person. Did I mention that we were not a wealthy family?

The crooks were really ready to kill us now. Not to get the loot, but because they were just plain mad that they had picked such a lousy house to rob. They made us press together and went into the opposite corner to have a summit meeting. Moments later, their greasy heads nodded, and the older began walking toward us. He slowly raised the shotgun midway between his shoulder and his hip. Only about ten or twelve feet separated us. Silence hung over the scene like a funeral pall.

Then He mumbled something and walked back to his partner in crime. Several minutes passed, and again he began walking toward us. I watched his partner close his eyes and turn into the corner before my own eyes fell shut. I was now enveloped in silence and darkness, waiting to hear the crack of the shotgun and feel lead ripping through me.

But the horrifying silence was suddenly shattered by cursing and a new command to get back in the house. I am not terribly fond of cursing, but the whole thing was music to my ears. I knew the angels had just won a big one.

As each of us made our way back to the fireplace, my father was again hauled off into the bedroom, and my panic resumed.

Cowards, I thought. *Don't have the guts to kill the whole family at once, so they are going to take out the leader and do what they want with the rest of us.*

This session was a long one. I began to wonder if they had asked Opa for his last words and he was responding by reciting the Encyclopedia Britannica to them.

After what seemed like a twelve-hour shift on a boring job, the door swung open and out came Opa. He was still white like before, but he had a strange, quirky smile on his face that looked suspicious.

"Honey, these boys are hungry," he said as he strode up to Oma.

I'm not sure who was more shocked–Oma or the bum's partner.

Just in case you have forgotten, all this happened three days before Christmas. The house was filled with all kinds of baked goods and other fattening stuff to eat. I thought it was kind of mean for Opa to try and kill these guys with Oma's cooking, but I was open to anything that would get them to put their guns down.

Oma spread everything in the house out on the table for them. After two or three bites, the leader of the twosome got up, stomped over to the refrigerator, and started rooting around. After a while, his head popped out just long enough to ask if we had any booze. The answer was No. Much to my surprise, he smiled and started back to the table. He had lost me completely. Halfway back, he stopped. Back to the refrigerator he went. Without even looking in, he said, "I bet you don't have any meat either, do you?"

The reply from my shocked father was, "No, we are basically vegetarians."

The now somewhat calm bandit sauntered back to his seat at the table, leaned his gun up against the wall, and mumbled under his breath to his partner, "You can trust these people."

If you think the whole situation fried my sense of reality and deleted a few megs of memory, I can assure you neither are true. We went from sheer terror to total bewilderment in the space of two minutes. We were still not allowed to talk to Opa. Therefore, we were in a total fog trying to figure out if this really was an answer to Oma's faith or if these guys just didn't like killing on an empty stomach.

When their meal was done, they dug deep into their pockets and slapped a twenty dollar "tip" on the table. Kind of made me think of April 15, when the good old pork-bellied government gives us a tax "refund."

Opa had made a deal in the bedroom that they could have one of our cars if they promised to leave peacefully. Opa also promised that we would never tell anyone about the ordeal or report it to the authorities. We would live our lives as if nothing had ever happened. And so, after two and a half hours, they took a car and left.

Now, I assume you are an intelligent person and are wondering why I am telling this story in a *book*, when Opa promised we would never tell. Opa lied!

Not really. I disobeyed!

That's more believable, but still not accurate. The truth is, the story isn't over yet.

The two guys left our house as promised. In town, they spent their evening's take on everything from cigarettes and drugs to instant oatmeal. A couple of hours passed, and they decided we could not be trusted. They got out the maps and agreed to come back and kill us if they could find our house again.

Meanwhile, we had thanked God for His miraculous deliverance and gone to bed. Not to sleep, but to bed. It was about 1:00 a.m. by now. The two guys were just beginning the ascent up the mountain where our house was hidden when, out of the blue, the car quit. An investigation the next day revealed that the alternator belt had snapped, and the car had ran out of juice. Once the juice quit, so did the electric fuel pump, and the engine ran out of gas, which is why the car ran out of juice. Got it?

If these idiots possessed one quality, it would have to be persistence. They got out and pushed that car for the next three miles, straight up the mountain. Not really. They spotted a house trailer not fifty yards away and decided to go "borrow" the owner's truck to go finish some work they had started in the woods up there on the mountain somewhere.

They barged into the trailer. Back in 1976, no one outside of city limits in Colorado ever locked their doors. We changed that. Fifty new locksmiths serviced the county for twenty-one years after our story was published. Sadly, we never got a commission.

Once inside the trailer, they found a mother and her infant sitting on the couch waiting for hubby and dad to come home. For the record, the family's last name was Love. No joke. Their name did not fit their characters. Mrs. Love told them her husband had the only vehicle and would be home any minute. Since they had time on their hands, they decided to search the trailer for more treasure. Since their first stake-out had gone bust, maybe they would have more luck here.

While one was in the back room pillaging, Mr. Love came home and walked in the front door. He was greeted by a lone gunman, whom he quickly smacked upside the head with one of those old flashlights that had a seventy-five pound battery hanging underneath it. The fight was on!

Hearing the commotion, the partner in the back room came running out and, without a moment's hesitation, fired at both of them. It was a fast shot, high and inside. He immediately opened fire with the second barrel. A curve shot, wide to the left. There was no time to reload, so he pitched the gun and jumped in on the action.

Mr. Love was able to get a table on top of both of them and made a beeline for his truck. Like all good native Coloradans, he had his own gun hanging in the rear window. Just as he was reaching for the gun, he saw the robber come to the door of the trailer and raise the single barrel shotgun. The moment he ducked, the guy fired. All the glass was blown out of the cab of the truck. Mr. Love escaped the main blast but did get a bunch of buckshot in his chin and shoulder.

If we had only known these guys were such lousy shots, we would have jumped them ourselves and gotten to bed a lot earlier!

It was time for the boys to reload both guns, and since Mr. Love now had his gun, they scratched the idea and started running. One shot in the air brought them to a halt. Mr. Love had them crawl back to the trailer on their hands and knees, like rats eating cheese. As the two would-be robbers ate dirt, Mr. Love quickly called the police.

So you see, we kept our word. We did not call the police.

The law enforcement boys arrived at the scene of the shootout. Would you believe, parked not fifty yards away, was our car? Four minutes later, a squadron of police cruisers, vans, and investigators ascended on our house like D-day. We were as happy to see them as children are to see Santa Claus. That didn't last long. We were suspects. It didn't take long for us to tell our story, and they found fingerprints to back it up. The thugs got a ride to the crowbar hotel, and we have lived nervously ever after.

What did we learn from this whole ordeal? Several things. Life is short, and eternity is long.

Sins that seem so important and fun one minute quickly lose their luster when death shines its haunting light on them. No one but God knows for sure, but chances are Leo would still be on the broad road that leads to destruction if it were not for that night. I heard and saw him cut a deal with God that he would serve Him forever if his life was spared. A vow he has been faithful to ever since.

And if the guys had shot us during the first half hour like they did at the Love residence, Mary would have slammed full-fledged into eternity thinking the whole thing was a joke.

I like to enjoy life, as this book bears proof, but we are living in serious times and, as such, need to ponder eternal life on a daily basis. Most of all, I learned that of all the things demanding God's attention that night, He had the time to brush aside all the trees, find our lonely house, and send His angels to camp around it and answer my mother's prayer.

Then again, it was way past time for God to hit my rebellious brother Leo upside the head and make him tolerable to society and safe on our streets!

"O God, for Thy bountiful blessings I do truly give Thee thanks!"

GAS

CHAPTER

7

High School Daze

Education. That wonderful word politicians use when they want you to vote for them. Well, it will sure be a wonderful day when schools finally get all the money they need and the politicians have to hold a bake sale to buy a new limo—don't you think?

Most leadership in this country can't do anything, so they attempt a career in teaching. And since they can't really teach, they get a degree in doing nothing. And since they can't do nothing real well, they usually become vice president.

"Blessed are they who go around in circles, for they shall be known as big wheels." What can I say?

After getting my life together at age fifteen, I still couldn't find a United States high school that wanted me. So my mom somehow snuck me into British Columbia, Canada, to an academy where I enjoyed four wonderful years. I can't speak for the staff there, of course.

After making my way up to Canada, I felt at home in beautiful British Columbia. The school was wonderful, and as I arrived, I was

told to report to the principal as soon as possible.

I'll never forget meeting "Mrs. E," as she was affectionately known. She invited me in for a brief interrogation.

"Welcome to our academy, Leo. We've heard so much about you! I would love to get to know you better. So tell me, Leo, what is your life's greatest ambition? What are your aspirations, your greatest goals and dreams?" Mrs. E looked at me with a pleasant smile, her eyes wide with anticipation.

"Wow, that's a hard question!" I replied, "Really now, I'm not sure. I love guns, rodeo, fishing, would love to be a famous cowboy, own a ton of horses and cows and pigs and chickens, but my greatest dream? Well, I'm not sure. Wait, I do know! I noticed when I arrived today that you have such a lovely daughter; I think I'll be dreaming a lot about how to win her affection, how to steal my first kiss, and eventually be suave enough to marry her!" I smiled, amazed at my own brilliance.

Mrs. E appeared, for a moment, to have suffered an infarction of some sort. She rose slowly from her chair, her face twisted in a strange contortion and said, "My daughter? *My* daughter? What do you mean, *my* daughter?"

I must admit my first meeting with Mrs. E made me a bit queasy. However, in our many sessions over the years, I was able to really relax and have a great time discussing with her my grades and various other items. Often, I left her office in a state of good cheer, throwing out one last witticism while Mrs. E would put on a show of weeping uncontrollably, at which she excelled. She could have made millions as an actress.

Life at a dorming high school wasn't bad. Oh, sure, there were guys who were gifted in minor atrocities, but most of it was innocent fun. Like the time I was asked to burn a carcass.

The school owned a small dairy, and one February morning, a cow gave birth to a little premature calf. The poor little thing froze to death in the 30-below-zero winter. When the farm manager discovered it the next morning, he asked me to take it to the dump and burn it.

No problem. I'm an expert in fireworks.

I fired up the backhoe, placed the little calf in the bucket, and on the way to the dump, loaded a five-gallon can of gas in the bucket as well. The snow was deep, and the air was so cold that when you spit, it turned to ice before hitting the ground.

The dump was covered with three feet of snow, so I had to search for a place to burn the carcass. Since there were no bare spots, I took the gas and sloshed some of it on the snow, making a nice burn area. Unloading the carcass, I sloshed some more gas on it, turned it over, and sloshed more on the other side. Before you could say, "Man, you're really dumb," I had all five gallons on the calf.

Then I stepped back three feet and pitched a lit match.

What happened next is hard to tell. Some thought it was heaven, others thought it was hell. The knowledge I gained at that moment, however, the knowledge that I could make explosions, had a permanent impact on my life, not to mention my anatomy.

I don't remember much after the explosion in the thin air. The initial bang was replaced by a thousand bells ringing in my head. The earth came back together, and the sky fell back in place as Mr. Rutland, the farm manager, came running up. He was normally a fine gentleman, only with a temper slightly shorter than a snake's hind legs. He took one look at the inferno and gave me a good tonguelashing, for some reason. I guess certain people just don't have a stomach for catastrophe.

I rather enjoyed the experience, and besides, no eyebrows and burnt eyelashes made for great conversation with the other students–especially the principal's daughter. She brought me plants, flowers, and sweets for several days while I recuperated. It was worth it all just to see her.

After such an episode, you'd assume I'd learned my lesson.

Wrong.

Scarcely had Mr. Rutland's advice ceased reverberating through my mind, when I was already plotting the next experiment with rearranging my anatomy.

The plan was hatched by Mr. Backfire. He was a suave gentleman who knew more about cars and motors than Henry Ford. His true identity must be kept secret, because through some unfortunate stroke of bad luck, my brother Squirrel fell in love with his daughter and married her! Therefore, we are now related.

The true story is that Mr. Backfire came so close to exterminating me that Squirrel felt the greatest way to show our family's gratitude was to marry his daughter.

My first introduction to Mr. Backfire was in our mechanics class, where he assigned us seats to learn auto mechanics. My seat happened to be an old battery. I learned that day that battery acid can eat the rear right out of a pair of Levis, and usually doesn't stop there.

Mr. Backfire then demonstrated to us the dangers of the cutting torch. He led us to the tanks of oxygen and acetylene and opened the two valves. Lighting the torch, he shot a flame ten feet long in the shop. It was impressive. Then he took a rag and snuffed out the flame. Gas continued to flow out of the torch nozzle as he took a plastic bread bag and filled it up with gas.

As the bag expanded, he tied off the end, closed the valves on the torch, and took us outside to a nearby field. Then he carefully laid the bread bag down, ran a trail of gun powder to the bag, lit it, and after a few moments the bag exploded with awesome force. Believe me, this stuff was potent!

We made several more bombs with Mr. Backfire in the next few days. They were especially beautiful at night, a huge orange glow would loom up with a deafening wallop, lighting up the area for a quarter mile. None of us could figure out what value such a class had, but then again, I guess students should always be prepared for the possibility of world war.

As Halloween rolled around, Mr. Backfire found himself concocting a great idea. If a little bread bag could make such an impressive explosion, what would a huge forty-gallon plastic trash bag do? The idea was quickly endorsed by three of us to create a massive bomb just for Halloween night. We would help build it, but Mr. Backfire was, of course, the brains behind the project.

And so it happened that Mr. Backfire, Curtis, David, and myself gathered on the eve of Halloween in the mechanic shop. Curtis held the big green garbage bag. I stood beside him as the torch was lit, the flame snuffed, and we placed it in the bag. Ever so slowly, the bag began to fill with gas. After fifteen minutes, it looked approximately two-thirds full.

"Wow, is this ever going to be some kind of bomb!" Mr. Backfire smiled, his eyes glazed over.

"Yeah, when this thing goes off, it'll wake up the dead!" David agreed with a crooked smile. The bag filled to three-quarters as we watched with glee.

Now, folks, glee is a good virtue, but when it plays second fiddle to your imagination, you can get into deep trouble. You see, inside the expanding bag was this little critter known as static electricity, and as the plastic bag unfolded, it created its own cute little internal spark.

I don't remember much after this point, except that there was a gigantic orange glow and an impact that struck with such force I was lifted straight up and thrown back ten feet against the garage door. A terrible bomb went off, and I was inside the bomb, streams of fire were going every which way—I was going every which way. The shop lit up like neon signs in Vegas while high voltage sang its death call. Then, everything went dark.

I became semiconscious of a voice several minutes later. "Breathe, Leo, breathe!" I couldn't see the person behind the voice and, quite frankly, didn't want to breathe. I felt like I was floating on air. It was so peaceful to just not breathe. I was never happier.

"Breathe!"

The school nurse hit me on the chest and began to kiss me, push my stomach and kiss me again. Now folks, I felt like I was *really* in heaven! Slowly my vision cleared and I looked up to see the school nurse hovering over me. "Thank God," she murmured.

I gazed around the room contemplating how I got from the shop into bed so fast, and it was then that I noticed quite a number of students and staff standing around. A few minutes later, I realized why their eyes were so wide open and anxious looking. I was lying in bed with only my Fruit of the Looms on! Somehow, between the blast and the nurse tending me, I had lost my britches and shirt!

Mrs. E came in about then, took one horrified look, and gave orders for all the students to leave the room at once or their virgin eyes would go blind! Her daughter was helping tend to my needs, but she had to go too. One thing about Mrs. E; she was a bit rough on the outside, but if you ever needed something, like a scolding or lecture, she'd sure give it to you!

Well, needless to say, I got patched up at the local animal hospital with the rest of the guys. After a few months, the bells stopped ringing in my head, and I was back to near normal. I guess there are just certain people who constantly look as if they are in dire need of help—and I'm one of them. Did I mention that I continued to be the official spokesman for the Band-Aid corporation and that following this event, their stock went up 151 percent?

The only good that came of this was the principal's daughter got to tend to me again. I purposely tried to remain in as bad a shape as possible, and it paid off. She wrote me her first love note while I was recuperating, and we had a wonderful time without her mom knowing (*Har . . . har . . . har . . .*).

For the first few years of high school—at least what parts I can remember—the days were wonderful, and I enjoyed each one. My education was expanding rapidly with knowledge, wisdom, and experience.

I learned that experience is what you get when you don't get what you want. I learned that if you can get others to believe your foolishness, you'll be very successful. If you believe it yourself, you'll be dead.

I even learned the five steps of a successful executive. I can still remember them.

First, study to look very important.

Second, always speak with great assurance, sticking closely, however, to generally accepted facts.

Third, avoid arguments. But, if challenged, always fire an irrelevant question at your antagonist and purposefully polish your glasses while he tries to answer.

Fourth, before talking to someone you want to impress, check out his solutions for current world problems. Then advocate the same strongly.

Fifth, when asked a question you don't have an answer for, give the person a "Have you lost your mind?" stare until he looks down, then paraphrase the question back to him. It works every time.

I also learned a lot about sales and business lingo. Such as:

"Advanced design" means it's beyond the comprehension of the people selling it;

"All new" means its parts cannot be exchanged;

"Developed after years of research" means it was probably discovered accidentally;

"Energy saving" means only when it's turned off;

"Improved" means imported;

"Lightweight" means it will fall apart; and

"We'll look into it" means "We hope you'll forget about it too."

As you can see, my academic achievements were beyond imagination.

The highlight of each school year was our annual campout. Once each fall, we were given five days to enjoy the bliss of the mountains and forests away from the books. Considering myself to be an expert in this area, I never expected any problems.

Wrong again.

Mr. Rutland was our leader. His way was the only way. If anyone was ever foolish enough to question his authority, his face would instantly turn red. Slowly his eyes would widen, his nostrils would flare, the buttons would snap off his shirt like shrapnel from his seven-foot height.

We were never intimidated but were always glad for the escape route between his massive legs.

Mr. Rutland felt that before we could go on the annual camping trip, he had to qualify us by "hitting the wall." No one could go on this five-day trip till he was man enough to "hit the wall." This consisted of hiking and running up a steep mountain without stopping till you passed out. I thought Mr. Rutland had hit the wall once too many times and told him so. Shrapnel flew like fireworks. Lucky for me, Mrs. E got wind of this and put a stop to Mr. Rutland's foolishness. However, we still had to follow his rules—no backpack over thirty pounds, no tennis shoes, no matches or canned food. It was worse than boot camp.

At last the big day came. A hundred miles of mountain wilderness in five days lay ahead. We started out early, and by ten o'clock we were hoofing our way up a mountain so steep the trail was only fifteen inches from my nose. We all started out quite optimistic but then shifted to the normal backpackers routine:

One foot is put ahead of the other. You breathe deeply, check your hip strap, wipe the sweat off your face, take a drink of water, eat a piece of dried fruit, take a picture of a chipmunk, check the map, and then repeat the process the next step.

Due to such a routine, we arrived high up in the mountains at a crystal-clear lake about midnight. The wind off the mountains was howling as Larry and I bravely attempted to erect our tent. When it was completed Larry gave me a funny look. "I thought this was supposed to be a *two*-man tent? Isn't that what the label says?"

We were amazed to find the two-man tent was made in Africa by two Pygmies who must have been on exceptionally good terms with each other. We both crawled in as best we could while the wind blasted us from all sides. I enjoyed a sleepless night imagining how well the tent would work as a hang glider.

Camping is *so* much fun!

Our wilderness survival skills were perfected by Mr. Rutland over the next few days. I learned to build a fire with flint and steel, rubbing two sticks together and using a Bic Lighter I sneaked in. I studied the art of camp cooking, while millions of mosquitos competed for attention.

Soon I was serving up hearty meals of five-pound pancakes, charred potatoes, flaming beans, and cocoa with mosquitos. I even taught myself to eat it. It really wasn't so bad. I learned to simply give a little shout before each bite to allow any insect or other creature a chance to escape.

One lazy day, Larry and I were looking over yonder at a snow-capped peak and decided it was a mountain to be conquered. Looming high above the valley, it seemed to constantly tempt us. Between it and our camp were three other mountain ranges, but we figured we could get there in three hours. Which we did—only it was three prophetic hours.

As we finally reached the summit, it was about seven o'clock in the evening, so we quickly headed back, hoping to make it to camp before dark.

"Isn't the trail this way?" I asked Larry.

"No, it's this way," Larry replied. "It *was* that way, but I know a short cut over these two mountains." Larry pointed.

"You've got to be kidding," I replied, "those mountains are sheer cliffs and solid ice glaciers. There's no way we can make it!"

But Larry insisted, and before long we were hopelessly lost in the forest.

"Do you have any idea where we are?" I asked cautiously.

"Of course, I do. Now quit your whining. The mountain is just up ahead over there." Larry sounded exasperated as he pointed.

Two hours later, I asked again, "Where is that mountain?"

"Listen, Leo, the mountain is not where it was before. That's not my fault. If a mountain wishes to change its location, there is absolutely nothing I can do about it!"

By now it was clear that Larry was suffering from high altitude sickness. Darkness was less than an hour away, we had no warm clothes, no matches, no shelter, and there were tons of wolves and grizzlies who were just dreaming of having Larry and Leo on the grill.

Pressing on through the gathering darkness, we finally came to the first mountain just in time to creep over its side on our hands and knees. A sheer cliff fell thousands of feet on one side while a granite wall rose another thousand feet on the other.

Believe me, all atheists should go through such an experience. We could win them all to Christ. We wouldn't even have to teach them to pray–it would come automatically!

As darkness closed in, accompanied by an icy chill, I found myself scaling a precipice on the second mountain as we headed in the general direction of camp. Larry lagged behind to see if it was safe. About halfway up the frozen cliff, I paused to look at a loose rock in my hand and suddenly recognized it as the rock that was supposed to be holding me on the side of the mountain.

My career in space was long enough to allow a lot of time for reflection, although nothing of great philosophical importance. In fact, the reflection was rather simple, "Man, is this ever going to *hurt!*"

Upon impact, I heard Larry yelling somewhere a thousand feet above me, "Leo, are you OK? Leoooo . . . Where are you?"

I counted my bones and yelled back, "I'm OK, Larry. I might have been hurt, but some rocks cushioned my fall. Come on down!"

After a few hours, Larry managed to find another route, and we were once again united in the darkness. Ever so slowly, we hobbled in the direction of the camp, and at about one o'clock in the morning, we arrived. The camp was deserted. No one was in their tents, and the unattended fires were dying.

"Where do you suppose everyone is?" I asked as I added wood to the fire.

"Beats me," Larry replied, "Must be off on some nighttime training mission Mr. Rutland dreamed up."

We fixed ourselves some hot cocoa and sat by the roaring campfire. I love campfires. You can watch them for hours. Simple little dramas being played out by the dancing flames. Most are reruns of previous campfires, but it's possible to change the channel by poking the flames.

"It sure will be funny when Mr. Rutland and the boys get here and we got out of whatever survival training they're doing." I commented. Larry laughed. "Yea, and when they all come back, we should really rub it in. We laughed together and proposed a toast of hot chocolate to our ingenuity.

Around three in the morning, the guys all stumbled into camp with bloodshot eyes, totally exhausted. When they saw us, they blinked in astonishment.

"Where have you two been? We've been out all night looking . . ."

"Looking for what?" Larry asked. "Looking for edible mushrooms?"

"*Har har har!*" We laughed together till our sides ached. "We got out of whatever you poor guys had to do! Har har har." Soon everyone was laughing, even Mr. Rutland. He loved a good joke, but rending his garments while pouring ashes over his head was really going a bit too far, I thought.

Needless to say, we all survived survival camp and arrived back at school only fourteen days late. I arrived at the local hospital where the nurse took one look, smiled and said, "It's so good to see you again, Leo. We were expecting you sooner or later. Why, what's it been now, three weeks since your last catastrophe?" I nodded. "Well, come right on in, no need to register. We know your medical history by heart now."

The doctor came puffing in a moment later, took one look and cried, "Oh no, it's you again!"

I always appreciated his kind words and told him no more compliments were needed. It was the least I could do to keep his hospital in business. My parents were especially proud. You wouldn't believe all the letters and phone calls from them constantly reminding me that they were sending more money to the hospital than the school!

Well, now that I'm an old man and approaching the midpoint in life, I look back at those days with amazement. It's a wonder we're all not six feet under! The brazen foolishness of youth is something God must have put in us, yet, when you look back, you realize how many times God looked down from heaven and shouted, "Gabriel, get over here quick! My boy down on earth is about to self destruct again! Save him now!"

Between the choking, drowning, electrocuting, falling, bombs, poison, lynching, starving, gunmen, grizzlies, snakes, accidents, airplanes, and Homo sapiens, you begin to realize it's only the hand of a heavenly Father that carried you through.

I suppose it would be easy to get presumptuous. But if one thought would ring true, it would be this one: "*If there's anything certain about life, it's the uncertainty of life.*"

I'm sure that's why Solomon says to "Remember your Creator in the days of your youth." Most of us, as we look back on our lives, would see multiple times we could have bit the dust. But God still delivered us. God does this to teach us that our lives are not our own. We belong to Him. If He has saved you from sin as well as certain death, then the purpose of your existence is to live for Him. You owe a debt of gratitude.

I have several friends who waited too long. They died, like all of us will someday. Some never even began to live for Christ. I wonder where they will spend eternity? Maybe not in heaven. So I guess that leaves only one option. Now that I think about it, they were pretty stupid.

It's like the time we discovered a black bear with two cubs down in one of the school's recently harvested wheat fields. Deciding to have some fun, a dozen students piled into a pickup, drove to the field, and began chasing the bears. As we pursued them over the hills and dales, one of the cubs went totally berserk and made a run for a nearby pine tree. He scrambled to the top while the mother and brother bear ran over the edge of the hill out of sight.

We all stopped to laugh and shout awhile and stood gazing at the cub in the tree. Suddenly, I was struck with a brilliant idea. Why not catch the cub up in the tree? Without thinking (one of my best virtues), I grabbed a limb and started climbing. When I got to within five feet of the cub, it began to bawl and climbed higher. The students cheered me on, so I climbed higher.

Finally, the cub was as high as he dared to go. I inched forward as the students yelled and screamed below, the cub bawled, and I paused briefly to enjoy the view. Seventy feet high in the tree, the view was lovely. Mountains to the left rising in splendor, the school neatly perched on the hill ahead, the fields of gold behind me, a huge black bear running my way. I blinked, but the picture didn't change. It looked like a six hundred pound freight train was due at the station in about three seconds!

Mama bear was on the run to rescue her baby from some imbecile who was trying to catch it. She was built like a nail keg, quivering flesh, teeth popping, hackles raised, her temper slightly shorter than a gnat's hiccup.

Lord have mercy, I knew I was about to meet my Maker.

"*YEOWWWAAGGHHEE!* THE BEAR'S COMING!" I howled and pointed at the six hundred pounds of fury. "STOP HER!"

Panic seized the students. Time stood still. Then, suddenly, everything broke loose. Students took flight in three directions—two guys and one girl jumped in the pickup and had the sense to drive straight toward the on-coming mama bear to attempt to divert her. I began trying to figure out how to jump out of a tree without ending up in the hospital again.

I don't remember much of the trip down, except that it was mainly vertical. The first thing I noticed, after regaining consciousness, was that I was running like a fast motion picture, wearing only my Levis. Something like a deer was bounding through the cornfield ahead of me, and I hoped it was a deer and not the bear, because I was gaining on it. It turned out to be the truck, and I dived in.

You would think things couldn't get worse, right? Well, just about the time I dived in, the truck struck a skunk. Things can always get worse, believe me. We had to bury it. Now that I think about it, we should have buried the skunk too. My shirt remained in the tree for several years as a constant reminder to not be so foolish again.

In other words, there are things in life that are just plain stupid, and we shouldn't have to wait till we nearly die to figure it out! Hatred is stupid. Racism is stupid. Premarital sex is really stupid. Alcohol is stupid, drugs are stupid. Movies with violence, profanity, and nudity are definitely stupid.

Friends who lead you away from God are quite stupid. Pornography is stupid. Music about drugs, sensuality, and the occult is plain stupid. Not getting an education is very stupid, being lazy is stupid, and not following the Bible is extremely stupid! Perhaps the most stupid thing is to go through life and never serve God. Gain all the world has to offer for seventy or eighty years and miss eternity, now *that's* the epitome of stupidity!

So let me encourage you to take three smart steps, wherever you are in life.

First, begin a thirty-minute daily devotional life with God, and make it your top priority. More important than eating, work, school, your boyfriend, girlfriend, or spouse. Use Matthew, Mark, Luke, and John for this and a good book like *Desire of Ages* by Ellen G. White. Always make sure the book has "Pacific Press" on the cover, or you might end up with an inferior book. Become mighty in the Scriptures.

Second, find your ministry, and start to use it. Far too many of us have skills, talents, and gifts, and we use these only to make money and serve ourselves. If you are in school to be in a professional field like medical, business, law, etc., then ask God how you can use that to be a missionary.

Every professional's office should be a pulpit for leading people to Christ. Every professional's home should be a church where a small group meets and shares God's Word and prayer in some way. If you are a manual laborer, you have endless opportunity to meet people, build friendships, and do social activities to lead people to Christ. Start some kind of ministry like a cassette ministry; a video seminar in your home or school; a fishing, biking, or aerobic club at your church. God needs all of us to be missionaries, not just warm a pew once a week in a dead church.

Third, make your life available to God so that evangelism and soul winning become a part of your life, not just a once-a-year event. Live to love others, serve others, and pray for others. Be willing to sacrifice your time, priorities, and desires to take up your cross and follow Jesus.

If we all followed these three steps, our churches would be alive, most problems would cease, and we would be in love with Jesus, rejoicing in salvation. And we would probably be in heaven.

Well, needless to say, I finished high school, much to the chagrin of many who bet against the odds of it. Mrs. E and her good husband remain dear friends, although I never did get their approval to tie the knot with their daughter for some reason probably evident in this chapter.

Mr. Rutland got shipped off to the Far East somewhere after my first year, but I can assure you, it was not my fault. Mr. Backfire is still alive, although he still swears that hearing aids don't work. The hospital is still going, and they always send cards at Christmas saying they miss me.

High school is certainly one of the best times of your life. If you're going there soon, or are currently enrolled, make all the memories you can, because you will look back on it with joy the rest of your life. If you are old and beyond high school, the fact that you're reading such a book as this shows that you're still young at heart. So, live as if Jesus were to come today, but enjoy life as if you were going to live here forever.

CHAPTER

Tree Planting

After my high school logging days, a chain of circumstances directed my life in a new direction. I became a conservationist. Not to be confused with a conversationalist, a name by which most folk know me now. A conservationist is one who becomes aware of God's creation. He becomes impressed that this earth, spinning around the sun, is a fragile planet. It's something God has entrusted to our care. Man's abuse of its natural resources has resulted in a gradual deterioration of our waters, forests, and lands.

Along with this conservation awareness, there arose another great concern in my mind. The high school's abuse of my monetary resources had left me in a gradual deterioration of clothes, car, and wallet!

And so it came to be, one day, that I heard about the gold rush movement of tree planting. A wonderful way to nobly do your part to help conservation, while fattening your own wallet. I joined for six months and planted in excess of a quarter million trees—most of which have probably died.

Several high-school buddies were also led on by prospects of fast money. We all teamed up in Colorado and made a grand caravan heading up to Montana for our first job.

I had purchased a nice custom van for $2,800 from a pastor who had compassion on a poor, destitute high-school graduate. It had a bed, microwave, electrical hookup, and water storage area. The kind of van you never drive up to your girlfriend's home for your first date. The rest of the caravan included two other vans, one pickup with a camper, and one old Lincoln Continental. All this became home for a group of guys who would have been safer living in a hornets nest that just got stepped on.

I got out the map and discovered another one of life's important lessons. Road maps tell you everything you need to know except how to fold them up again! At any rate, one fine day we headed down I-70, and I was leading the caravan. The air was crisp and clean, Mozart was playing a lullaby over the stereo, and the cruise control was set at 69 mph. "Ahhhh, life is soooo peaceful on the road!"

"*Whaam!*"

I awoke suddenly to the sound of Mozart playing rock and roll at such a pitch that it sent me bouncing all over the cab. Peering over my feet which were now comfortably resting on the dash, I looked out in wonder at the scenery.

Wow! What a transformation! From asphalt to grass and corn. The highway department should have put some signs up! I thought.

I sped past a farmer on a tractor who was waving wildly and pointing north. I waved back but began to have an uneasy feeling all was not well.

Upon full recovery of my senses—approximately half a second later—I realized I was past the right median and running through a corn patch with my cruise control still on! The highway was just off to my left, about two miles away. With corn stalks battering my grill and mud slinging into orbit, I cruised on over and got back on the asphalt, rolling to a stop. The rest of the caravan pulled up behind.

"Great stunt, Leo. For a minute, I thought you had fallen asleep," David said.

"Man, that was wild! I never saw so much mud fly in all my life! How'd you do it?" asked John Paul.

"For a while there, I thought you were going to roll that van," Larry said anxiously. "Can you show us that again?"

I blushed, not expecting such compliments.

"Tell you what, guys, maybe a rerun later. We'd best hurry on. I see the farmer coming."

We drove on. A person just has so much luck, and when you use up such a big dose all at once, you don't want to fritter away the little bit that's left. It was the only time I've ever fallen asleep at the wheel, and it really was a pleasant experience. Everyone should try it at least once. I highly recommend it.

We arrived in Montana ready to do our noble part for the environment. A beautiful meadow high in the mountains became our campsite. As the creek wound its way through the meadow, the evening sun dipped below the trees. Darkness came quickly. The stars twinkled above. My buddy John Paul put the final touches on his tent and began to fix supper. John Paul believed in living well. Tons of food were stored in his car. The smell of refried beans, cheese and crackers, soup, and potatoes filled the evening air. I looked in dismay at my grub and decided I needed a wife.

The greatest adventures in camping always came from my own extraordinary cooking. Trying to eat what I made was even more adventurous! The sight and smell of it were enough to give an indiscriminate skunk a severe case of Montezuma's Revenge. Being a bachelor, I tried hard to eat healthy but figured observance of all the health rules would probably cause me to live longer than I could afford to anyhow. So, I just made do.

This is why all the guys liked John Paul. He was a great cook. Before long, everyone was stuffed with John Paul's cuisine, and we all hit goosedown with full stomachs to hibernate a while. That is, everyone except a large family of bears who inhabited the area, all of whom were suffering with a severe case of malnutrition and acute irritability.

COWBOYS MAKE BETTER PREACHERS

While peacefully sleeping about midnight, I suddenly heard a most awesome scream amid the clatter of pots, pans, and growls of delight! Peeking outside my van, I noticed John Paul had moved his tent thirty feet up in a large spruce tree. He was yelling in a language I wasn't yet acquainted with. The bears didn't seem to mind the expletives and systematically tore apart boxes of cereal, pancake mix, dried soup, cheesecake, and cookies.

We finally coaxed John Paul out of the tree the next morning and surveyed the damage. He decided he needed a wife too.

Our introduction to tree planting came quickly. We were outfitted with backpacks consisting of a large aluminum frame. Into this frame, large Styrofoam blocks slid down from the top. In these Styrofoam blocks were thirty round holes about the size of a quarter and six inches deep. These were filled with soil and each had a cute little spruce tree growing out of it. Ten blocks filled the backpack with 300 trees.

Next, a "dibble stick" was awarded to each of us. This was a five-foot contraption with a wooden handle and a steel tip shaped like a spear. A small step near the bottom stuck out six inches.

"OK, you guys listen up." The forestry woman in charge of us spoke with authority. "Rule 1: Shut up and listen. I only talk once. Rule 2: It takes a lot less time to plant a tree right the first time than to explain why you didn't do it right! You got it?"

We nodded our heads together as she continued.

"You take your stick like this and cram it into mother earth like this." With a great thrust and a grunt, the dibble stick sunk deep into the ground. "Then you stomp on the step like this," another grunt and the stick sank farther into the ground. "Now you twist the stick and pull it out and you've got a perfect hole." She smiled as we all gazed in wonder at the perfect hole. A nearby mouse looked on, and you could just see his wheels turning as he planned to make that hole into his new condo.

"Reach behind your back and pull out a block of trees."

We obeyed.

"Now you pull out the tree with the soil and all the roots and drop it in the hole like this." The little tree fit nicely as she dropped it in. "Now, the last thing you do is take your boot and kick the earth around the tree real hard so it's in there tight. And you just made yourself nine cents!"

Our minds raced. *Nine cents! Three hundred trees times nine cents. Why, that was nearly thirty dollars a backpack!* The mouse held up a protest sign about the evils of capitalism.

The woman lowered the train whistle she used for a voice and finished by saying, "Now plant them ten feet apart all over this entire mountain. Go straight up, and when you get to the top, go across till you run out of trees."

Dave and I led the pack as we all took off up the mountain, pounding trees in every ten feet. At approximately tree 250, we reached the summit. The view was spectacular, but we missed it since our only thought was the thirty dollars we would make when we unloaded our first pack. At last, the final tree was neatly plopped into the earth. We looked at our watches.

"David, that took less than an hour! That's thirty dollars an hour! We're gonna be rich!"

We ran all the way down the mountain for our second load and by day's end had planted 3,000 trees each.

As the sun sank in the west, we dragged our limp bodies back to camp. We held back the tears bravely as we washed down cold sandwiches with hot cocoa. We hit goosedown early with every fiber of our few flabby muscles screaming in pain. The local coyotes sat in bewildered silence listening to the mournful wails coming from our camp.

But we were rich! Three hundred dollars a day wasn't bad. While some of the guys quickly spent their money, I remembered Opa's advice. "The quickest way to double your money is to fold it over and put it in your back pocket." Amazing as it may seem, dads do know what they're talking about sometimes!

The next morning, we managed to crawl out of bed, and after half an hour plus three boxes of matches, we managed to get a fire going.

"Where's John Paul?" David asked. "I'm hungry."

I shrugged. "Must still be in bed, I reckon. Let's see."

We found John Paul in his tent—completely immobile except for his eyes and mouth, both of which were twitching vigorously. Since we couldn't make out what he was trying to say, we carried him out between us. His body was frosted over and as stiff as a two-by-four, so we just leaned him up against a tree till the fire warmed his bones and he started functioning again.

Such is the life of a tree planter.

During our first adventure in the Northwest, an early winter frost ended our labors after six weeks. So we moved to happier hunting grounds in the south. Arkansas and Mississippi were warm, inviting, and needed a lot of trees.

Having grown up in the West, it took some adjusting to understand the South. A "mountain" down South is any bump that is over sixty feet tall. "Breakfast" is boiled peanuts with grits and biscuits. And y'all means "everybody!"

The South had famous football teams whose fans wore masks with big hog snouts (at least, I think they were masks).

I heard talk of "the new south" and "the old south." But the major difference as far as I could tell was that one drove Japanese pickups and the other didn't. "Dixie" is a popular word, and everyone loves you if you have a rebel flag displayed in the back of your pickup. Be sure not to mention the word "Yankee," and you'll probably do OK.

The people of the South are known for their "southern hospitality," and they are quite nice folk. I did discover one major difference, however, between them and people of the West. In the West, folk generally are downright honest in their hospitality. They speak their mind, and you always know where you stand.

Now in the South, everyone is hospitable, but often insincerely. They might say one thing to you and turn around and say the opposite to someone else. They may invite you to "come on down anytime," but if you do, you find out they didn't really mean it.

Now don't get me wrong—there are a lot of good folk down South.

It's just a general observation. No, I'm not prejudiced! OK, yes I am! West is still best!

We were soon situated in the "woods." The South doesn't really have forests, rather, it has a lot of hardwoods. Oak, chestnut, hickory, and the kind of foliage that attracts lots of chiggers, mosquitoes, ticks, and water moccasins. Here we got acquainted with the new crew we were assigned to and in this crew one of the most memorable characters I've ever met.

P.J. was a tree planter in his early forties who had a definite aura about him—a presence that seemed to linger long after he left. I think he took a bath once in the summer but not quite as often in the winter. He was a true hillbilly—a man who ate possums, didn't believe in many modern conveniences, and didn't understand words like "income tax" or "Visa."

On the door to his trailer was a plaque that read: "I hope that after I die, people will say of me, 'That guy sure owed me a lot of money!' "

We all sat for hours scratching chiggers and listening to his tales of adventure in the hills of Tennessee. He was a lonely man, trying to fit a simple life into our modern society. I can still see him shake his head slowly and say, "Boys, I jest donnot git it! Why does alla life got ta besa differcult?"

P.J. was a life saver, however. On one fine morning, we were planting trees in an old swamp area. P.J. was planting just ahead of me, dressed as usual, and I was working hard to get upwind of him. P.J. always carried two holsters into the woods. One held a .44 magnum pistol, in case he saw some free food hopping around. The other held his sandwiches for lunch. After spending a few lunches together, I determined the .44 magnum was probably safer than some of his sandwiches.

While pounding in trees around some deadfalls, I suddenly heard P.J. roar like a wild man, "Dontcha step over that log!"

Actually he said a few other words that made the angels blush, but while trying to filter out P.J.'s language, I hesitated in mid-stride. A second roar went off. P.J.'s .44 magnum echoed over the swamp, while my eardrums rang.

"Waugh, lookie here!" P.J. smiled his toothless grin. The seven-foot length of a fat cottonmouth curled up as P.J. held it high. Its head was completely missing since having come in contact with P.J.'s .44.

"I done saved yer life, son!" P.J. grinned widely.

I smiled my appreciation.

"Yessir, you'da been fixin to meet St. Peter at dem pearly gates b-now iffin it hadn't been fer me!"

I smiled again, trying to indicate my gratitude.

That was the turning point in our relationship. P.J. was the hero, and the story was recounted a hundred times. The snake grew to over twelve feet long, P.J.'s gunshot grew from ten feet away to seventy-five. I grew from six feet away to six inches from certain death. I played along, knowing it made P.J. feel good, and worthwhile.

P.J. never would discuss God or the Bible. Somewhere in his past, he had been wounded by a so-called Christian. I tried to share God's love, His power, His ability to bring peace, but P.J. would always stop me. So I just tried to live it. We grew close, and come April, our paths came to a crossroad.

Sitting in P.J.'s camper on our final night of tree planting, we talked and laughed. It was time to say "so long," and as I got up to shake his hand, P.J. said to wait. He went to the cabinet and pulled out a little gift. It was a church he had built with hundreds of little pebbles all glued together.

"This here's fer you. I tain't religious at all, but you'ns done been good to me. I done seen the good Lord a workin in yer life. It's been an insperation . . . Yer fixin to be a preacher boy, so I thoughts ya might like to havin yer first church." P.J.'s eyes were misty, and I was feeling a bit emotional too.

"Thanks, P.J., don't reckon I've ever received a finer gift, I'll always cherish it."

"You promise to say a prayer for me when yer memory gits to itchen?" P.J. asked with his head bowed.

"I'll pray for you everyday, P.J. In fact, I'll pray for you right now."

And so I did. It was the last time I ever saw P.J. A few years later, some friends told me P.J. had died. I hope he's sleeping in Jesus. Somewhere beneath that rough exterior was a heart. That same heart is in every person. Everyone needs love.

Sometimes the only love you will know on earth is God's. Others will only know God's love through you. Real love is defined in 1 Corinthians 13:4-7:

"Love is very patient and kind, never jealous or envious, never boastful or proud, never haughty or selfish or rude. Love does not demand its own way. It is not irritable or touchy. It does not hold grudges and will hardly even notice when others do it wrong. It is never glad about injustice, but rejoices whenever truth wins out. If you love someone you will be loyal to him no matter what the cost. You will always believe in him, always expect the best of him, and always stand your ground in defending." (*The Living Bible*).

Make it your daily practice to measure up. Someone's last chance to see what God is like may be through you.

BIBLE
HOW TO DO EVANGELISM

CHAPTER

Cowboys Make Better Preachers

C.D. is one of the most intimidating preachers you'll ever meet. If he had ever appeared in the movies, Clint Eastwood would have been happy to be his baby brother. The first time we met in Colorado, C.D. eyeballed me with his penetrating beady eyes. His massive build and fiery red hair had a way of making you feel a bit queasy. After swallowing a few times, I managed to squeak out a few words of greeting. C.D. didn't seem to be impressed.

C.D. was a tough customer. Growing up through a troubled youth, his cowboy style of dealing with life got him stuck in some badlands, and he led a life that would have made Eastwood look virtuous. That is, until he met God, who took his life, changed him, and made him a great preacher.

Perhaps a bit like the apostle Paul, C.D. retained his distinctive way of life in the ministry. His no nonsense attitude of "gonna get that ole devil" colored his entire philosophy of ministry. He used to love to fight. He now stays busy fighting the devil and, occasionally, pastors and members who act like the devil. I'm amazed he's not pushing dandelions yet. God employs extra angels to look out for the likes of C.D.

In the middle of all this is his wife, whom I'll call Patience. She's a sweet southern gal who somehow fell in love with a restless keg of dynamite. She knows how to handle C.D., and God made her special to be able to live with him. I recall her saying once to me, "C.D. is like a barbwire fence. He has his good points!"

As soon as C.D. reads this chapter, I'll have to do a crusade overseas and let him cool off a while. Then sometime later in Oklahoma, we'll sit under a tree, drink lemonade, he'll blow his steam a while, and everything will be OK.

I reckon we were a strange pair in evangelism. I was his "trainee," and he was my boss. We were just enough alike to get into trouble a lot—which made for great education. Church administrators seem to agree. Since my training with C.D., it's been especially amusing to meet conference presidents and secretaries who cordially invite me out for a meal and then ask, "And where did you receive your training for evangelism?"

"Oh, I trained with C.D."

Suddenly a look of horror passes over their faces as they choke on their vegeburgers.

"C.D.?" they gasp.

"Yes. You ever heard of him? Big guy, beady eyes, red hair, cowboy-type?"

They look slantwise at each other while I pretend not to notice that their faces have turned beet red. Cold beads of sweat form on their brows and drop into their decaf. They look as if Clint Eastwood just hit town. Carefully wiping their faces with their paisley neckties, they clear their throats and ask, "How long did you train with him?"

"Oh, roughly thirteen months—it depends on if you count the time we've spent in the hospital and in jail together . . ."

By this point, they are usually headed for the nearest pay phone to call 911. Sure is nice to be associated with someone so popular!

C.D. was tough on me and didn't take any flack—which is probably why I liked him. Two-faced, political, lily-livered, liberal preachers always made me a bit nauseous. If there was a problem, C.D. let you know in language that was graphic and down to earth.

For example, a typical preacher when dealing with a smoker would say, "My dear friend, in our committee over the last six months, we have observed that you are struggling with the problem of inhaling the poisonous herb of tobacco. Now we understand this is very difficult, but God will help you. Our computer analysis says you're a type F personality, and we have now analyzed your spiritual profile with our professional psychologist. We have a lovely twelve-step program and a five-day plan we would love for you to attend to help you overcome this in the future. Won't you come?"

C.D., on the other hand, would follow a more simple plan. Backing the smoker into a corner, he would look him in the eye and say, "Man, you got a problem! You smoke like a chimney! Your breath stinks, your clothes stink, and all you're doing is burning your money up. Now, you're not stupid, and smoking *is* stupid, so let me give you God's five-minute plan to quit right now and you can have instant victory!"

It worked. Like C.D. said, "If a man's got a wart on his nose, don't tell him he's looking good. Tell him he's ugly and needs to get rid of the wart!"

C.D.'s first assignment was for me to get a motor home. He roared one day, "You can't run with me until you learn how to live in a motor home on the road!" Well, now, a motor home at $30,000 just ain't the kind of investment a typical young fella fresh out of high school can make.

After I pointed this out, C.D. said, "Well, son, that's your problem; I ain't gonna take care of your problems. I got enough of my own. Get with it! It'll put some grit in you. Now get to work—no one ever drowned in their own sweat!"

Since I had only a few thousand dollars, I decided to sweat and pray.

My prayer was answered a few days later when Opa and I were running around Denver buying parts for his auto business. This was always an enjoyable time for us. We would drink a lot of pop and eat chocolate while agreeing not to tell Oma. Not that Oma would mind, it's just prudent to avoid sleeping out on the porch in your long johns in the dead of winter with starving mountain lions around. Good judgment comes from experience, you know, and a lot of that comes from bad judgment.

Driving to a parts center in Denver, we noticed a nice 22-foot Winnebago motor home being towed in the yard. Its side was totally caved in from an accident. It looked rough, but I instantly knew this was my home on the road. Closer inspection showed that the frame, drivetrain, motor, and tranny were in perfect shape. It looked like a herd of buffaloes had run through it, but in reality, it was in need of minor repair.

From the agent, we learned that it was supposed to go up for bid in the next auction. Opa offered him $2,000 cash for it right then. Somehow, the details were worked out, and two hours later I had a motor home!

We limped it home illegally down Interstate 25. People would whiz by and point at the huge hole in the side. It was embarrassing, but I don't reckon today anyone remembers. The rear wheel finally gave out on the mountain near home, and Opa towed it the last seven miles. Oma came out to see, and I could see she had her doubts, but she cheered us on anyway.

Things progressed rapidly, and in a few days, the hole was fixed, the new aluminum skin was painted, and you couldn't tell the thing had ever been hit. The total repair bill for parts was under $700. It was a minor miracle. But then again, ain't God just like that?

During this time I was also concerned about finances. My forestry and construction funds had been used to buy a car and now a motor home. I had only twelve hundred dollars left. So, we prayed again.

A few days later while visiting another parts store, Opa met with "Earl" the owner. They were formerly acquainted, but today Earl was bubbling over with excitement. He had just been to church and "got saved," as he put it. And now, he was on fire! Opa couldn't believe the change!

They talked about the Lord a while, and Opa mentioned about me going into evangelism. This intrigued Earl, and he immediately decided he was going to test the Lord to see if He really answered prayer. He looked at me and said, "I'll tell you what. See that rig over there?" He pointed to a Mercedes Benz. "I've been trying to sell that for over a year. Let's you and I pray. I'm asking $5,500. If the Lord sells it in one week, I'll give you half!" So we prayed. In my heart, I knew the Lord had it all planned.

Arriving home that night, we received a phone call. It was Earl. "Man o man," he drawled. "You done got a *hot* line to heaven! As soon as you left, a guy walked in here and bought that car–and paid cash! Come on and get your share!" We praised God together, and I went and got my cash.

You know, there's a good lesson here. One of the most frequent questions I get asked is, "How do I know God's will? How do I know I'm doing what God wants?"

It's really quite easy. Just follow three steps. First, figure out if what you're thinking or praying about is in harmony with the Bible, truth, or principle. If it's not, save your breath. If it is, then pray for God's continued providential leading.

Second, God gave you a brain and common sense. Use it. Figure out what you feel is the best decision, or the direction you feel is best to go. In other words, make a decision, and go forward to the best of your ability.

Third, pray; "God, I believe this is best, with the knowledge You have given me. If it is, keep the doors open; if it's not, slam the door hard."

Believe me, God knows how to do that! If the doors stay open, keep moving. If they close, go back to step one. Follow this, and you'll have a grand time seeing God work in your behalf.

And so, with a good motor home and plenty of money, I began evangelism. Arriving in Detroit, Michigan, for our first crusade, C.D. greeted me with a smile. "*Whyoogh*, I hope to shout!" he exclaimed. "Never thought you would do it . . . My word, I hope to shout!" He rambled on for a while as we recounted, over lemonade, God's providence. It was great to be in full-time soul winning.

C.D. "learned me the ropes," as he put it. Taught me about organization, preaching, preparation for crusades, and visiting folk. Always hard on me, he never said much in the way of appreciation, but you always knew he was on your side.

From Michigan, we traveled to California, and it was here I had one of my most memorable experiences with C.D.

For a while, C.D. had observed my country-boy attitude of trusting everybody and not locking my doors. It was a source of constant irritation for him. He'd set me down and lecture all about the crazy people in the world who steal and kill. "One of these days," he said, "you'll wake up and see some thug with a knife on your throat and gun on your head and then you'll wished you had listened!"

I tried to listen, but one particular day I forgot.

It was in December, and the church school kids invited me to ski with them. We had a blast! Going insane on a cliff with a pair of skis is almost as much fun as time spent on the hurricane deck of a cow pony. After a great day of snow and sun, I arrived to my motor home that evening, only to find water running out my front door! Wading in, I discovered a pipe had broken in the bathroom. As I think about it, it was one of the pipes my dad had fixed. At any rate, through the mess of it all, I was able to fix the pipe and get most of the water out. Since the carpet was wet, I took my electric heater and propped it up with a book so it could blow on the carpet and dry it during the night.

By now it was late, and the wind had picked up. The motor home was rocking a little, and I went to bed a bit concerned that maybe the electric heater would fall over. I could just imagine my motor home looking like Sodom and Gomorrah the next morning. I slept a bit fitful until about 1:00 a.m. Half awake, half dreaming, I was suddenly awakened by a loud *WHAM!*

Instantly, I knew the heater had tipped, and if I didn't hurry, I'd be toast in a few minutes!

Throwing aside the sheets, I hit the floor and stumbled down the narrow hall to the bathroom. In the darkness, I fumbled for the bathroom door when suddenly my hand touched something mysterious. Looming in the darkness was a huge shadow which suddenly came to life. A chilling wave of terror tingled down my spine.

YEEEAAAAAGGGHHH! The shadow screamed its rage at me!

My mop of hair froze straight up, while from deep within me I felt the most horrible scream I ever uttered come forth with equal intensity.

AAUUUYEEEEAAOOWOOO!

The next few moments were classic. I hit this shadow with all my might, and it hit me back. We staggered around in the darkness yelling and saying things that later needed to be thoroughly repented for. Finally, the shadow screamed at me, "It's C.D., Leo! It's C.D.!"

Finding the light switch, he stood there trembling and shaking, mad, and hotter than Satan in long handles! It took a while for him to pry me off the ceiling. Together, we collapsed on the couch. We both sat twitching and trembling like two chipmunks.

"C.D., I . . . I . . . I ought to *lynch* you! D-d-don't you *ever* try that again!"

"I-I-I was just t-trying to . . . to teach you a lesson, boy. You've got to lock your doors!"

After composing himself, he explained his actions. Arriving home late that night, he was about to turn in when he thought about his friend Leo and wondered if he had locked his door. Quietly checking the door, he was amazed to see I hadn't followed his counsel. Stepping inside, he decided to teach me a lesson. He hit the bathroom door, and the rest is history.

Well, we made a pot of counterfeit coffee and after an hour, its warmth soothed our shattered nerves, and we were able to laugh. He bade me goodnight, and I once again retired to bed.

C.D.'s trailer was next to mine and unbeknown to me, he was having a great time telling his wife all what had happened. I was just drifting off to sleep when he got to that awesome yell:

YEEEAAAGGGHHH!

The sound echoed from his trailer to mine. It shattered my

peaceful sleep instantly. It sure is embarrassing to pry yourself off the ceiling twice in one night.

Going out to eat was an event always characterized by embarrassment with C.D. He has a habit of loudly asking for the cook to custom make a vege-meal. Sometimes the least embarrassing place was under the table. I've spent a lot of hours identifying chewing gum under tables—how this factors into worthwhile ministerial education is anyone's guess.

On this occasion, we were with a pastor and his wife who were still adjusting to C.D. and his ways. On our night off, we arranged to go to a good Chinese place where the food was rumored to be excellent. The pastor's wife was a city-bred gal who had a flair for high fashion and for what Rush Limbaugh calls "Feminatism," otherwise known as the feminist movement. She sort of wore the pants in the home and believed a woman's place was in the House—and Senate. She and C.D. didn't see eye-to-eye on much.

Upon our arrival, we found ourselves at a table near the bar of the restaurant. Being as we were in cowboy country, high-fashion cowboys lined the bar and tables.

C.D.'s usual vocal sermons for the cook had made these cowboys set up and pay attention. One who had a few drinks too many swaggered over to C.D. and in a rough voice asked, "Who are you anyhow?"

C.D., never one to miss a fight, looked him in the eye and said, "I'll give you three guesses."

The cowboy eyed him suspiciously. "You're either a car salesman, a lawyer, or a lousy TV evangelist!"

C.D.'s lights went on in his eyes, and I could see he was running 220 volts. "*What* did you say?"

"I said a lousy TV evangelist!" The tipsy cowboy's voice was cynical.

In an instant, C.D. was on his feet. Jerking the poor fellow up by his shirt collar, he slammed him down in a corner of the bar. The air got tense quickly. The other cowboys looking on were ready to get in a brawl, when C.D. told them to sit tight till he got through saying his piece.

I don't remember a whole lot after that except C.D.'s opening words.

"Listen, man; I was once a drunk skunk like you!"

C.D. literally preached to him his personal testimony of how God had changed his life for the better. The cowboy listened with eyes wide open. The rest of the bunch relaxed, and a whole bar that night heard the plan of salvation. By the time C.D. was done, his food was cold, and we had already eaten. The pastor and his wife left early. No problem for C.D. He just called the cook to microwave his tofu and rice.

Evangelism is full of such adventure. There were times we were persecuted, followed by the police, shot at, robbed, and threatened.

I remember the Canadian meeting where, after being robbed and told to leave town, we decided to stay anyhow. The next morning, my car was egged, all the windows were broken, and everything was torn up. I telephoned C.D., and he came over complete with his brass knuckles.

He let it be known to all at the hotel that "if he ever caught the rascal who did this, he would inflict punishment upon their anatomy more severe than that of an inquisition rack!" For some reason, I never had any more problems. That's one thing about C.D. You could always count on him.

It was during this time I learned another important lesson in life. God loves diversity. I suppose He could have made us all the same, like mechanical robots with no personality or all one color, but God has created all for a different reason.

C.D. could reach out to outlaws and hardened sinners in a marvelous way that few were able to do. His wife was able to reach others C.D. would not appeal to. And I reckon the feminist pastor's wife had the ability to reach those kinds of people.

Simply put, there is no one single type of person who is the sum of all things. God needs diversity to reach the world. Your personality is your gift from God. Enjoy it, and remember, you're special, because there is no one else like you in the world! From the moment of conception, God had you all planned.

David wrote, "I will praise thee; for I am fearfully and wonderfully made: marvelous are thy works; and that my soul knoweth right well. My substance was not hid from thee, when I was made in secret, and curiously wrought in the lowest parts of the earth. Thine eyes did see my substance, yet being unperfect; and in thy book all my members were written, which in continuance were fashioned, when as yet there was none of them" (Psalm 139:14-16, KJV).

Think about it. From your hair color to your facial features, God designed you with your personality. No one will ever take your place in God's heart of love.

I used to think everyone had to be just so. Trying to "change the world" was a miserable task—I'm glad I stopped trying.

God gave some people the abilities to become brain surgeons—not exactly my cup of tea, but thank God for them. People like my brother Squirrel need them, you know.

It's easy to look slanchwise at folks who don't interest us or who think and relate differently to life. It's easy to say negative things or to judge them. However, I've found that there is a lot more pleasant way to live. Just remember two things.

First, be "positive." If your brain is not in gear to say something positive, don't engage your mouth. And second, "impute." Always impute the best motive to people's words and actions. Assume they meant it in a good way.

Use these two principles at home, school, work, and at church. If everyone did, the lowdown would rise up, the crooked would straighten up, the gossipers would shut up, and we would find ourselves at last in that place called heaven.

Remember, one person—*you*—can make a difference. Be all you can be for God's glory.

CHAPTER

Studs and Fillies

I will never forget the moment I first fell in love. It happened in a most unusual place. I was a young man of fifteen years who had recently been kicked out of high school for "having a bad attitude." Life was pretty simple, and I didn't miss the school any more than they missed me. My life with Christ was still a future reality. I found myself in church that day only because Oma wanted me to tape the sermon for a friend of hers.

It was a typical church morning as I sat in the back looking through the glass at everyone singing. Suddenly, as I was contemplating the mysteries of why chewing gum loses its flavor, there stood before me a picture of innocence and loveliness such as I had never witnessed. I blinked in astonishment. She hesitated at the door, her tiny figure a matchless picture of grace and beauty. For a brief moment, our eyes met, and I felt the most incredible rush through my innermost soul. Her entire presence captivated my young heart and emotions with such intensity that I trembled.

Woah! Get a hold of yourself, I thought to myself as I tried to pull myself together and picked my jaw up from the floor. But as usual, I wouldn't listen.

What is going on with you? You're supposed to be attracted to good-looking horses, not women! Who would ever trade the smell of horse sweat and leather for sweet perfume? Girls are soft and pretty, they don't get along with barbwire and hay bales . . .

But alas, it was too late. My young heart was stolen in an instant.

What young man or woman hasn't felt that first sweet taste of human love? Although young, foolish, immature, and new, it forever remains a special memory.

Desiree was a beautiful lass of fifteen years. Her golden hair was long, her form petite, and her face was angelic. I determined to win her affection, no matter what it took. This, however, proved to be a bit difficult.

First, because every guy around wanted her also. Second, my experience with the opposite sex was limited to female horses. Third, Desiree had a father who was big, broad, and really intimidating. His hands looked like two country hams capable of causing permanent brain damage. I was about as welcome in his home as a sidewinder in a cow camp.

Fourth, this particular church was part of an institution that was really strict. If you were caught even *speaking* to a girl, you were in deep trouble. They would haul you into an office and spend some quality time telling you how sinful it was to like girls.

However, my big break came when I heard that Desiree loved horses! She even had her own horse back in Oregon!

A few days later, after waiting around for three hours for her to leave school, I "accidentally" ran into her. Not being born shy, I asked about her horse. Her pretty little eyes lighted up, and her face radiated. We spoke for a long time. Her voice was soft and shy, reflecting her kind personality. I invited her to the ranch where I worked as we parted company. Although we had not spoken it, we both knew we were madly in love.

Before many days passed, Desiree arrived at the ranch. The ranch boss jokingly wolf whistled, Lenny, my partner, grinned, and in general, we had a grand time. Not knowing much of what to do in the presence of such a lovely person, I had been coached carefully by Lenny that girls loved to have you hold their hands and kiss them.

It was easy to hold her little hand—it was warm and soft. But how to kiss her? I'd once been accused of kissing my horse, which I didn't mind, although the horse had to undergo psychiatric help for several months. But how to kiss a young woman?

Our opportunity came in the grain room. It had a self-closing door, and suddenly we were alone. Puppy love was strong, youth is wild, and with the temptation of forbidden fruit, we kissed. And kissed again. Believe me, it was better than the horse.

Our affection for each other became obvious, and we soon found both parents strongly opposed to our budding infatuation.

"You're too young. You're not mature. You can't see each other again!" Oma and Opa said.

It hit the fan one evening as a church leader falsely accused me of improper conduct—things he himself was guilty of. My father, in anger, whoped me good that night. I didn't blame him, but I sure was mad at the whole bunch of church people. It wasn't a good thing.

Hate and anger is a prolonged manner of suicide. Don't *ever* let them control you. Sometimes sincere parents and leaders do make some dumb moves. They should have known this kind of attitude would only make Desiree and I go underground and sneak—we did. Meeting here and there in secret, we continued our relationship.

A few weeks later, the truth came out of how I had been falsely accused. The same leader who had accused me was caught committing adultery with another church woman.

I'll never forget Oma and Opa coming to me. It meant more than words to see *them* apologize. Then Opa and I had a man-to-man talk. He spoke of things I needed to hear and learn. He and Oma taught me that young women were to be treated with respect and honor. They were honorable, and it was my duty to never compromise a woman in any way. They taught me to never conduct myself in a way she or I would ever regret. They instilled within me a desire to be a real man and to make right decisions. I could tell they wanted my best. *Our* best.

They kindly asked me to just be friends with Desiree but not be in love with her.

"How?" I asked. "I have such deep incredible feelings for her. She's all I want; I love her!"

Oma and Opa understood the fact that at age fifteen, our hormones were going ballistic. But they asked me to trust their judgment. I could sense they really wanted my best, and I knew they knew what they were talking about. We agreed.

It was difficult for Desiree and me. One thought that Oma and Opa had shared kept burning in my mind. "You can't know true human love till you know divine love."

I didn't love God. I didn't even know God. Every fiber in my being wanted to shrug off that idea and go with my heart, not my head.

Not smart. It ends in tragedy. It's like a film that's been rerun a million times.

Act 1. Their eyes meet.

Act 2. Their lips meet.

Act 3. Their souls meet.

Act 4. Their attorneys meet.

Act 5. Curtains.

It happens to over fifty percent of people who marry. It makes sense to listen to parents and make right choices. More people make a mess of their lives in this area, than any other area.

Shortly after this, in a miraculous way, God got hold of my life and turned it around. I went back to school in Canada, still deeply in puppy love with Desiree. It was hard to leave her. How can you explain to someone you love that because you want the best for her, you feel like you need to go? To continue your education, to mature, and to make right decisions? And give her the same opportunity so her life can mature, and she will make right decisions? It's a paradox. Had we made right decisions to begin with, we would not have had to struggle so. We parted with a secret kiss.

In the following two years, we met on three occasions. She was back in Oregon, and we spent several days together between school breaks. Our lives were maturing, and our conversations reflected deeper things of life—religion, education, and goals. Desiree came up to Canada once also to the school I was attending. It was a cool fall evening. We spoke of our lives together, our hopes and dreams.

Although we couldn't find words to say it, the passing years had taught us we were not meant for each other. Our lives were going different, but good, directions. It was time to be honest and allow each other the freedom of choosing paths—paths not directed by our youthful puppy love and emotions. We said goodbye.

Her usually happy face was tearful. I shall never forget that parting. She stood there, a tiny figure in her pretty blue-and-white gunnysack dress. It was the last time I saw her. Time and life have moved on. Although we have never met since, I shall always treasure the happy memories we shared together. Our relationship had been a privilege for me. I hope and pray that wherever she may be, she is happy, for she was and will always be a very special friend.

The lessons learned here are for all youth. The passion and love one feels in youth is wonderful, but it comes with great responsibility. One choice can determine a lifetime of results— for good or endless heartache. It pays to listen to those who are older. It pays to make right decisions. It pays to use your head, not your heart when you are in love.

In the following months, I was terribly lonely. I missed Desiree. Throughout this period, I felt a longing that needed to be filled. A loneliness for a friend that was consistent. One that would fill a need for unconditional love. During this time, I met Christ—the desire of my heart.

A lot of folk know about Christ. They know so much about Him they make you sick. A lot of preachers know a lot about Christ—that's why you fall asleep with their boring sermons. Not too many *know* Christ. I mean really know Him as a wonderful person! He was God, but He was also an incredible human being.

He taught of unconditional love. He talked to prostitutes and made them pure. He loved children. He loved happy weddings. Wherever He went, He made people's lives a bit more pleasant. He taught folk how to forgive and forget, how to be long-suffering and patient. He ate with tax collector/IRS types and made an honest living working with His hands in a carpenter shop.

And even though He didn't feel like it, He went to Calvary to pay the price for my sin—death.

Then He rose to live again. *That's* fantastic!

In my mind, if I had been Christ, the first thing I'd have done was to march right back up to Pilate's judgment hall, push aside the guards, walk right up to Pilate, grab him by the throat, and say, "You little rascal, you thought you could get rid of me, look at me now! I'm alive! I told you!"

Then I'd have dropped him and gone next to the high priest. While he stood there trembling and shaking in his sandals, I'd have grinned in his face and said, "You see, I told you—in three days! You thought you and your Pharisees were indestructible on Friday, but I told you—*Sunday's* coming! Well, now I'm here!"

Well, the Lord ain't like us. Thank the Lord! Instead, Jesus appeared first to Mary, the little woman out of whom He had cast seven devils. That's the kind of man Jesus was. That's the man I met as I read the four gospels. He changed me. He changed everything. I fell in love with Christ. He became precious to me. Wonderful to me. Everything to me. And our love relationship began. It's never ended but gets sweeter every day.

This led to chapter two in my love life. Satisfied with Christ, I wasn't looking for female companionship, but it all happened one Sabbath afternoon.

I was in Wyoming working one summer for a construction company that built homes. Invited to a member's home for Sabbath dinner, I met "Buffy." Buffy was one of the most captivating young women in the world. She was exceptionally beautiful. With an ever-present smile, she was full of life and bubbling over with enthusiasm and happiness. More than her outward loveliness, there was an inward beauty that shone from her pretty face.

Buffy *loved* Jesus. I'd never met a girl like her. All she could talk about was Christ. Our kindred spirits made an instant bond of love between us. We enjoyed many happy moments together.

Everything was different now. It seemed everyone around us had us married already in their minds. The contractor who employed me employed her also. The visiting evangelist told us we were meant for each other. Suddenly, we found ourselves at the opposite end of the canyon. Now all the "multitude of counselors" were urging us together! Talk about confusion! Buffy had her head on properlike, but I was still wet behind the ears.

Things got a bit more complicated when the contractor offered to make me his partner in the business, since we worked so well together. Lots of money, a new truck, a new home with a sweet wife named Buffy—I was about to dive headlong into this once-in-a-lifetime opportunity when Buffy's mom and dad said something about finishing our education and going to college.

Buffy's dad was a preacher, by the way. This was back in the days when folk still listened to preachers. Probably too long ago for you to remember? At any rate, we listened.

It was a unique relationship. Our affection was deep, but pure. Our happiest moments were talking about Christ and dreaming of working for the Lord. The summer passed quickly. We made right decisions. We went back to finish our education. It was a happy parting. We hugged and kissed goodbye, everything was simple, sweet, and gratifying. In the months that followed, we wrote. We were still not sure of our future together.

In reflection, it was so unique. Buffy was simply just so lovable—kind of like a little furry puppy dog with big eyes. Everyone is drawn to it because it's so adorable.

Somehow, in our minds, we knew we would never be husband and wife, and yet everything was so perfect. It took me awhile to sort this out. In the process, there was some turmoil. A lot of people didn't understand. Some said we were "stupid not to marry each other." Everyone seemed to think God had us planned from the beginning.

We slowly were able to focus on the paths of our hearts. We were so much alike. Had we married, we probably would have had enough combined energy to start World War III.

We saw each other off and on in Colorado, Wyoming, and at summer camp in the following months and remained close friends. There was always an affectionate hug and tender moment between us. Buffy met a handsome young minister that summer at camp. Together, they went to college and fell in love. I still remember Buffy's call, announcing she was getting married. I was in Arkansas, working in the woods. From the pay phone at the campsite, we talked. She was so happy.

Hanging up, I took a long, slow walk by the lake. It was bittersweet. My tears fell unashamed into the clear water. I recounted all the happy moments we had shared. There was a part of my heart that was crushed, yet so happy for her.

"Dear God, thank You that Buffy is so happy. Bless her with every blessing of life and love. May she only know happiness and fulfillment in her marriage. Thank You for allowing me the privilege of sharing a part of her wonderful life."

More tears fell into the still water. The stars and quietude comforted my heart. Peace filled my soul. And another chapter of the wonder of love closed.

Life is determined by choices, to a large degree. Sometimes it's fair, sometimes not. The advantage of belonging to Christ is that it makes no difference. He is in control, and all things work together for good.

There was a third chapter of love in my life that will remain unwritten. Why? Because it's a part I still do not understand. A part that has a lot of painful memories. It's one of those occasions when you utilize the proverb, "Never miss a good chance to shut up!" I still find myself at a loss to put it in perspective, let alone on paper.

I mention this in passing simply to share another meaningful insight. Even when we do our best and follow all of God's principles and make right decisions, things do not always turn out as they should. That's because in life there are others besides us. God loves them too. And in the triangle of life, sometimes God has to do the best for all involved in the situation.

It's like the farmer who earnestly prays for rain for his parched fields. But there is also the evangelist who earnestly prays for good sunny weather so people will come to his crusade. God may send the rain to the farmer because it's more important for all involved. As an evangelist, I can get mad at God and ask Him why He ruined my crusade with all the rain?

But usually if I do, God opens the windows of heaven farther, until people are using canoes to get to the meeting! It's better to trust Him. And as the song says, "We'll talk it over in the by and by."

This unwritten, third chapter of love begins in Colorado. My education completed, I was beginning training for full-time evangelism. The evangelist I worked with informed me early on that I needed to get serious about a good wife, because evangelism is near impossible without a helpmeet.

My heart was committed to a young woman whom I had known for several years. It was during this time of training that a decision had to be made in our relationship. The memories are sad ones, as it seemed all the providential doors shut over and over. There was a final attempt one day to move our relationship in the direction we both wanted, but due to a difficult parental situation, it seemed impossible. The bitter memories created by her parents ended one day with deep pain. It was not her fault, she was a victim. Caught in a web of family, spiritual imbalance, and situations far beyond our control, our relationship could not progress as planned. As I said, I still do not understand it.

Driving away that evening from her home, I felt totally crushed and wounded. As the sun began to set, I experienced the most frightening moment in my life.

The mountain road I was driving on narrowed at a deep canyon where sheer cliffs dropped to the pounding river below. Parking the car, I stopped and got out. The pain was too much to bear, and I wanted to end it. Standing there a long time, tears blinding my vision, I cursed God, I cursed her parents, and felt an overwhelming urge to jump.

Suicide is totally foreign to me. I had never, ever, even thought about it. I'm probably the most optimistic, life-loving person ever born. But that one moment was different. I almost did it. It was scary, painful, and my heart broke as tears of sadness, anger, and longing fell together. For several hours, I wrestled with it. Finally, with trembling steps, I walked back to the car, and there, totally exhausted from the emotional struggle, I slept.

The morning sun shining through the windshield greeted me. The sweet melody of songbirds filled the air; the freshness of morning dew was dripping from the green grass. I awoke slowly, realizing I had slept all night. Suddenly, the world looked different. Walking back to the cliff, I knelt and prayed. It was good to be alive.

Although this relationship had ended in such sorrow, I knew God was still in control. All things would work together for good. I prayed that God's will would be done and for His guidance in such an important decision. For the first time, I surrendered this area of my life to Christ, and asked that He would send that special someone into my life in His time and way.

As time passed after this traumatic experience, God brought Tamara into my life. We knew of each other in Colorado, but never had spoken much nor seen each other for many years. After several years of struggle in the former relationship, I was not ready for her totally.

But I found in Tamara a love that was unknown. Tamara loved me. That may seem elementary, but relationships in my mind had always been a one-way road. I would love her and live to make her happy and fulfilled. And if she could put up with me, that would be a minor miracle!

All that changed with Tamara. She told me that she loved me from the start; she believed in me and supported me. Her parents were the same. They loved me, unconditionally.

Here I learned another important lesson of life—one I needed to learn. Love is a two-way street. It is wonderful to give. It's also important to gracefully receive.

Tamara, in her ever gentle, quiet way, took my heart, healed the former pains, and lovingly touched my life. She was mature beyond her years. Her strength of gentleness, her unsolicited affection, her Christlike character and purity flowed like a mountain stream to soothe my soul.

Tamara was the essence of love. She was beautiful and petite. Her life, was so simple and uncomplicated. Her tiny fingers made the piano come to life and her voice sang softly as she ministered to the congregations. She was amazingly talented at everything she attempted.

She was also an incredible cook and kept me well-fed, which was a major blessing. My cooking career as a bachelor was limited to God's original diet–fruits, grains, and nuts–better known as peanut butter and jelly sandwiches.

In short, Tamara was sent by God, at just the right time. Our love progressed without a single hindrance. God had prepared us both for each other. We tied the knot on September 18, 1983. And its been a honeymoon ever since. It's worth doing it God's way!

I owe everything to Tamara. She made me an evangelist. She supported our ministry. She always gives 110 percent. Never could I have dreamed of such a wonderful woman. Through the years of toil, constant travel, and seldom being home, she has never complained. Her love is as fresh and constant as it was the first day we met.

I'd like to close this chapter thanking God for a most precious wife, lover, and friend. It was worth it all to make right decisions and to allow God to choose that special person.

"Delight thyself also in the Lord; and he shall give thee the desires of thine heart" (Psalm 37:4).

Can I hear an "AMEN"?

CHAPTER

11

Brothers and Friends

Herman Schreven

There are a lot of brothers in the Bible, most of whom never got along—Jacob and Esau, for example. Either Jacob was a master con man, or Esau wasn't firing on all eight cylinders. Seriously, if Leo had ever tried to get me to sell my inheritance for a mess of beans, I don't think I would have fallen for it. (By the way, this is Squirrel again.) Leo and I are true brothers, but the only way we might be like Jacob and Esau is that Leo has a hairy chest and mine is smooth. I tell Leo that's because hair doesn't grow on steel.

From an early age, we always did everything together—mostly work. By age three, we had our Ph.D. in garbology and had to do household chores regularly. By four, we had our masters in gardening and ranching, with a B.A. in hoeing. By six, we had begun the building trade, taking after our father. We built go-carts, beds and furniture, slingshots, bows and arrows, and most other stuff that never worked. By age seven, when most boys dream of baseball and Nintendo, we longed for chainsaws, Craftsman tools, and sledgehammers.

Our fascination with building new houses began at the tender age of zero score and eight years. It was then that we built our very own, armor-plated tree house. The armor plating resulted from an exceptionally high NSI rating of seventy-three.

NSI, for those of you who aren't treehouse aficionados, stands for "Nails Per Square Inch." We happened to run across an abandoned fifty-pound box of roofing nails, just as we were beginning our quest to build a tree fortress. We had hit the mother lode of every child's nail-pounding dreams!

There were so many nails in our first treehouse, the inspector couldn't even see the timber. In fact, the tree had more nails in it than pine needles on it!

The best thing about our first construction project was that we didn't need a permit from the county to build it. We didn't even need our parents' permission. At least, that's what we thought.

When Opa came home and saw the mutilated tree, we learned our first lesson on dealing with building authorities when you have circumvented the law! No failed building inspection in future years was as painful as that first oversight. The only advantage for me was that Leo was still the older and I could plead ignorance, so he got the punishment.

One day, a local contractor spotted our very raw talent and hired us both for ten cents an hour. We had finally hit pay dirt! Five and a half hours of work would give us the buying power to own a chocolate bar-free and clear. A mere 750 hours of hard labor would pay for a snow ski. Another 750 hours and we would have a pair of skis. Boots, bindings, poles, and lift tickets could all be earned in the following years.

The contractor who so diligently trained us had but one simple, primitive rule of thumb. I committed it to memory in its entirety. I will now recite this gem of truth, the contractor's creed of conduct, the passion and conviction that made this man the craftsman that he was. After working five minutes on a project that should have taken five hours, our mentor would stand tall, square his shoulders, pick the sawdust out of his eyes, raise his chin a notch, and proclaim

"It's as good as any."

We were awestruck the first time we heard this proclamation. It was the word *any* that left things wide open. Good as any what? Any treehouse? The stuff he had us building would have failed miserably against the treehouse standard. Good as any doghouse? The doghouse would win in both quality and aesthetics, no bones about it. Good as any mud hut? At least that was close enough to have a good argument about.

His "houses" were built on slabs of concrete that were as smooth as the shining sea in the eye of a hurricane. You could actually put a basketball on the floor of the kitchen and watch it roll around the house like it was in a pinball machine.

All in all, we didn't learn or earn much in those first experiences of building real houses. There is a right way and a wrong way to do every job. At least, we had mastered one of the ways. If you don't know how to do it right, at least you know one way not to try!

Our illustrious building careers were put on hold for several years, until we both ended up at the same boarding academy. It was a brand-new school that had almost no housing. It was also a rather conservative school that didn't have time for sports and other such forms of physical exertion. Half the day was spent in school and the other half at real work.

The school also brought new meaning to the term "room and board." Their philosophy was simple—they provided the boards, and we built the rooms. Now, building your own housing may seem like a pretty raw deal for a teenager in high school, but it actually had its advantages. We built secret compartments in the walls that were totally undetectable to the unsuspecting eye. We then hid everything from stereos to candy in those walls. The candy worked out fine, but the stealth stereos were a total disaster. The school was so far removed from civilization that we couldn't even pick up static!

On one particular day, Leo and I were working on the second story of a new house which we were building by ourselves. Leo was rattling around in the rafters and encountered a board that he felt was in his way and of no vital importance to the house. He yelled at me to find the resident Skil saw and pitch it up to him. I may not have known much about building yet, but I did know how to follow orders, especially when Leo was the one giving them.

I promptly found the desired tool and heaved it up to him. He impatiently grabbed the saw in one hand, the soon to be circumcised board in the other, and tore into it with the usual gusto that accompanied all of Leo's activities. What happened next, I'm not exactly sure. Somehow, while sawing, Leo managed to cut a nice, deep eight-inch canyon down his wrist and across the palm of his right hand—which is really strange, because he's normally right-handed.

I saw the saw go sailing across the wide blue sky at the same time Leo fell down the ladder. He was yelling something about how soon he was going to die if I didn't get the truck and haul him to the hospital right now!

I must say, it was all quite dramatic. He had succeeded in cutting open some pipeline in his hand that let out an awesome burst of blood each time his racing heart would beat. I was impressed! Leo always has had a knack for doing things all the way and to the utmost. If there was a cut to be made, Leo would be certain to do it better than anyone else!

While beholding all this, my system got a quick burst of go-juice as I sprinted up the hill for help like a jack rabbit in a brush fire. I got to the truck just in time for Leo to throw me in the cab and yell "GO!"

There was one slight problem, however—I was fourteen years old, without a driver's license, and in a foreign country. None of this seemed to matter to Leo, who was doing all he could to try to keep the little bit of blood he had left in his body. I quickly found a qualified driver, designated him, and we were off.

Fortunately enough, we found the only faculty member who still had a few wild hairs left on his balding scalp and knew how to drive fast. The closest hospital was fifteen miles away, and he drove like Dale Earnhardt on steroids. Except for my brother bleeding to death, I was having the time of my life. We were breaking every speed limit within fifty miles combined, and we had a bleeding passenger who was certain to make any lawman look the other way.

We got Leo to the hospital alive, and after twenty pints of my blood to replace his, he was on the slow road to recovery. It's a chilling thought, isn't it? My blood in Leo's veins—have mercy!

Between bomb blasts, construction accidents, and a multitude of other near-death experiences, it's a miracle that Leo made it through high school alive. It has been a secret for years until now, but the real reason Leo never went to college is because he was afraid he wouldn't live through the first semester of his freshman year.

Several years later, after we had forgotten everything we ever learned about building, except for how good we could be, we decided we were still pros and struck out to build a house for Leo's would-be future in-laws.

By this time in the chronology of Leo, he was madly in love with a fair maiden named Tamara. A plot was born of pure genius, mixed with a generous portion of hormones. Together, we would build a splendid house for the parents of the lovely Tamara and accidentally leave one bedroom out. Tamara would be left destitute and roomless, at which time the dashing Leo would offer her not just a room, but an entire house of her own (if she would but marry him). I may not have all my facts straight on that one, but they're close.

After intense negotiations, an agreement was reached. Leo and I would build the house. Leo would get his bride, and I would be paid the going rate in cold hard cash. After years of drought, Leo and I were in business again. We learned how to move walls, staircases, ceilings, and floors on that project. Our MVT (most valuable tool) was a barbaric, crude utensil called a cat's paw. A simple tool with only one purpose in life—to pull nails.

When this nifty tool was combined with the raw power of a sledgehammer under the skillful direction of a frustrated brother, no wall was safe. There were walls we moved seven times. Sometimes because we put it in the wrong place to begin with, sometimes there were other contributing factors.

One hot, sticky, sweltering day, we had an unfortunate mishap while putting in the windows on the upper level of this fine structure. We each had a ladder strategically placed on either side of the gaping six-foot opening where the window was to be placed. Slowly, we tiptoed up the ladder, holding the glass bomb in one hand and the ladder in the other. Somehow, we managed to stay in step as we climbed our respective ladders.

Upon reaching our destination, we were about to set the fragile apparatus in place, when I lost my grip on the window. Leo let out a yell that could best be described as a mountain lion having open-heart surgery without an anesthetic. The window ripped a nice chunk of his finger off as he desperately attempted to save it (the window!).

To no avail. We both reeled as we watched it free fall fifteen feet to the ground below. There was the expected shattering of glass, and we rushed down to see how badly it was injured. Wonder of wonders, only the outer pane of the double-paned glass had shattered. To this day, I don't know how, but the inner glass stayed in one piece!

We quickly picked out the shards of splintered glass from the outer window until all that remained was a perfect single pane window. We both looked at each other in startled amazement and in perfect harmony proclaimed, "It's as good as any!"

Scampering up the ladders with our new, improved, lighter than the previous model window, we put it in place, nailed it, and in moments the job was done.

After all was said and done, Leo got his bride, his in-laws got their house, and I got my money, which I quickly blew while dating Tamara's younger sister.

Our conscience bothered us a little since we knew the window was defective, but who would ever know? As the weeks and months passed by, we completely forgot about it until one cold winter night. The in-laws had invited us all up for hot chocolate and games. We were having a grand time trying to win a game of "Pictionary," when Tamara's father shivered and said, "*Brrrrrr!* I always get cold sitting by this window!"

Leo looked slanchwise at me and by the look on his face, he was hardly able to contain his laughter. Tamara's father pushed the curtain aside to have a peek at the window. "Look at this, guys. All the windows in the house are clear, but this one always ices up; do you have any idea why?"

Well, it was confession time, and we had to tell him the whole story. The window stayed in place, but we learned the truth of the old saying, "You can be sure your sin will find you out!"

Over the years, that saying has proven true. I've seen it a lot. People cheat on their tests, and later on it catches up with them when they try to find a job and are not qualified. Or, someone is unfaithful to their spouse and a year later find out they have AIDS. It's easy to fool people on earth, but sooner or later it comes out. If not now, on judgment day.

Having experimented for years on school housing and a home for the in-laws, Leo figured he knew enough about construction now to at last build a real house of his own. After all, he was married now, and Tamara desperately needed a room. Leo conned me (with a few bucks) into helping him on this project and the promise that if I ever found a girl who would marry me, he would help me build my own house. He figured it was a safe bet.

As we began, it appeared we had picked up a few tricks from the previous ventures. If any building project can be considered normal, Leo's abode was as uneventful as could be expected. The only glitch, or I should say glitches, were the times a county inspector showed up.

Leo has about as much tact and patience with inspection boys as Sadam Hussein has with Kurds. The main reason being, these inspectors always want to be tipped a few hundred dollars. Leo wouldn't hear of it, and so the inspector always faulted things that were perfectly up to code. This would then result in Leo heading to the county commissioner to file a complaint. By the end of the home-building process, the inspectors were really being nice to us.

We did run into one challenge when we were attempting to put up the ridge beam for an eighteen-foot ceiling. We tried everything to get that beam up in the sky, but to no avail. At last, Leo spotted a tree growing not more than ten feet from the house. We promptly nailed the ridge to the tree at precisely the right height and hung it out to where we could attach the first rafters to it. It worked like a charm.

To this day, the tree and the house still stand. I call it Leo's treehouse.

Fast forward three years and you will find me at the altar gazing into the most beautiful set of blue eyes a man could dream of. As soon as I said "I do," my eyes shifted for a moment to Leo, who happened to be the minister performing the ceremony. I immediately let him know that it was time to settle a bet and build one more house.

It was the only bet Leo ever lost. There was only one issue to be settled. Who would be the boss? It was to be my house, but I was the younger brother and had always marched to his drum, and a pretty fine drum it was. To be honest with the historical facts, Leo did spend a couple of summers working with a real contractor, which did give him more experience than I. Combine that with three years of seniority, a gap I have never been able to close, and Leo had the inalienable right to boss me around and bark the orders.

Time and several houses had turned us into a pretty dynamite duo. In exactly five weeks of eighteen-hour days, we built a very respectable three bedroom, two bath, two-car garage house from concrete to ceiling. We did every aspect of the house ourselves, and it was the crowning jewel of our labors together.

After applying the paint and wallpaper, it stood up on its own, and I sold it a few months later, before the first winter's snow. It was as good as any. Since then, we have continued to build here and there, and if he ever quits preaching, I think we could make millions building "as good as any" homes.

There is one area I put Leo to shame in, and that's skiing. He was such a great instructor that in no time I could out-ski him. Since we were so poor, our first skis were wood, with cable bindings. Our all-leather boots came from the Goodwill department, and we carved our own poles from ponderosa pine. We learned to ski on a hill near home.

Awaking one morning to a new snowfall, I found that Leo had

already beat me to the hill. A fresh pair of ski marks were cut in the snow, back and forth through the trees. Near the bottom, I noticed the ski tracks went on both sides of a tree. Then I found the two skis, without Leo attached. Pondering the probability of such a phenomenon, I ascended the hill to find that Leo had made a huge impression on the tree. I mean, this tree was really moved. Leo cannot only sway audiences, he can sway trees too. It took a lot of care, but finally the tree survived.

Another day at one of our favorite resorts, Leo and I were practicing our downhill speed skiing. This was our specialty, and more often than not, we had our ski tickets revoked for speeding. We usually reserved speed skiing for the last two hours of the day, so if the patrol got us, we still had put in a good day.

It was while practicing such a run that Leo and I split down parallel trails that met at the bottom. I was doing 70 mph when some guy crossed my path. The wipeout was extraordinary, and in the process, my ski cut a deep gash in my forehead. Blood gushed out–I passed out. A few moments later, the patrol was headed my way.

Leo was blitzing on down, and when our trails crossed, he expected to see me and continue racing. When I didn't show, he slid to a stop and looked back uphill. When he saw that I was down, he quickly popped off his skis and started to run up the mountain. When he arrived, the look on his face was a mixture of pain and deep concern. He thought I was about to take my last breath.

I was actually OK, but the blood gushing out of my head had covered my face and froze. Frozen blood, in case you don't know, turns black. And so my face looked all mangled, black and red, and like something out of a horror show. Leo didn't realize this until the patrol had sledded me down to the hospital.

After a few hours, I was as good as new, and we drove home in the dark. It was a new day in our relationship. I realized how much Leo really loved me and how much I meant to him as a brother. It is a good feeling to know there is someone you can count on.

In the Bible, Jesus is also called our elder Brother. He, too, knows us and is concerned about our welfare. I reckon God gives us relationships here on earth to help us understand our relationship to Him.

As brothers and friends, Leo and I have shared a lot of disasters. Biking, for instance. From an early age, we had an obsession to jump bikes. In fact, we even composed a song to the tune of "We Are a Missionary Band."

The words went like this: "We are the dirty double diggers, the dirty double diggers, the dirty double diggers, we are the dirty double diggers, spinning all we can." Yes, I know it sounds corny, but to two 1960s seven-year-olds, it was better than the Beatles.

We learned to build awesome ramps (inspired by Evil Kenivel). Our jumps grew from thirty to forty feet. By age nine, we hit fifty feet. Age eleven got us to sixty feet and at last, at the ripe age of thirteen, Leo made it seventy-four feet! Everyone was impressed, except Opa and Oma. They kept saying we were going to kill ourselves someday. They were right.

A few days after achieving immortality, Leo was attempting to break seventy-five feet. From the top of the hill, he barreled down the gravel road to the ramp, pedaling as fast as his skinny legs could go. He stood up as he hit the ramp, pulled back on the handle bars, and believe it or not, the bike went over eighty feet!

Leo, however, only went thirty-seven feet, plus twenty-eight more if you count the part he slid on his rear end. It was quite amusing. The bike sailed sweetly by in perfect form, even landing on its wheels.

Leo also sailed by, about fifteen feet high in perfect form, holding the now detached handlebars. The look on his face said, "Man is this ever going to *hurt!*"

Needless to say, the impact left Leo with a pair of britches that had the seat clean eaten out. But it also had its benefits. For two weeks, Leo didn't have to go to school, since he couldn't sit down. It is rumored he still has gravel in his hindquarters.

When the Bible says a good friend sticks closer than a brother, I'm led to believe it's true after all the years. Leo and I are both brothers and friends. I've heard a saying that if you go through life having made three true friends, you are fortunate. We all know lots of people, but few have really true friends.

The Bible is full of good examples of true friendship—like David and Jonathan, or Jesus and John. In their friendship, they found someone whom they could trust completely, always count on, and be themselves with, without worry of being judged or criticized. Everyone needs a friend like that. You can always find it in Jesus, but He also gives us relationships in real life to encourage us along the way.

As I turn the corner into my thirties, I now value friendship more than almost anything. If you have a close friend, thank God for that person, and value that friendship more than gold.

As I ponder all the adventures in life and construction Leo and I have shared, I am reminded of John 14:1-3, where Jesus promised that He has gone to prepare mansions for us in a land of endless glory. I'm grateful to worship a God who is personal enough to build that first mansion for me. After all, my experience with celestial mansion building ranges from limited to non-existent. I'm thankful that Jesus is not leaving it for me to blunder my way through that first one.

Beyond mansions, I praise God for the work He is doing in my life. God Himself has stated in His holy word that He is the Author and Finisher of my faith. It is good news to realize that, when it comes to my salvation and my mansion, Christ is the Master Builder.

THE
PREACHER

Final Words of Wisdom

In a Prophecy Seminar

On Sowing Wild Oats: "You don't have to jump into a sewer to find out that it stinks!"

On Smoking: "See this ten-dollar bill? See this Bic lighter? See the ten dollars go up in smoke? See how dumb you are when you smoke?"

On Atheists: "Have you heard the new "dial a prayer" for atheists? You call a number, and no one answers."

On Stubborn Sinners: "Why folks are so hell-bent on going to hell I'll never understand, especially when salvation is free!"

On the Bible: "The Bread of Life never goes stale!"

On Clean and Unclean Meat: "You say everything is clean in the New Testament? OK, here's a guy at Calvary with a ham sandwich. He's sad because that ham is unclean and he's hungry! He impatiently waits for Christ to die. As Jesus takes His final breath, the guy shouts a grand 'Hallelujah! My pig was just cleansed!' Then he wolfs down the sandwich. Now, folks, does that make any sense?"

On the Holy Spirit: "The same sun that melts wax, hardens clay. Ain't the sun's fault, it's the material it shines on."

On Heaven: "There will be three surprises when you get there. 1. You're there. 2. You thought a lot of folks who are missing would make it for sure. 3. A lot of folks who you thought would never make it are there!"

On the Judgment: "Repent now, avoid the rush on judgment day!"

About Mom: ______________________________

About Life: "Life is what you make it. You will find what you are looking for."

The Tribulation: "You haven't heard about the seven-year tribulation? Don't worry, God hasn't either."

On Tithe: "You think Christianity is restrictive? You ought to try marriage! God only gets ten percent. She/He gets fifty percent the minute I say 'I do!' "

On Reputation: "If you lie down with dogs, you'll pick up fleas."

On Salvation: "When I look at myself, I don't see how I could ever be saved, but when I look at Christ, I don't see how I could ever be lost!"

Leo Schreven

On the Secret Rapture: "It appears that the secret rapture of the church is so secret that even God doesn't talk about it."

On the Law: "God didn't call these the Ten Suggestions."

On the Devil: "Next time the devil reminds you of your past, just remind him of his future."

On Death: "Let's talk about Lazarus. He's dead four days, his body stinks. Jesus says, 'Lazarus, come forth!' Lazarus waddles out with all the grave clothes wrapped around him. As they unwrap him, Lazarus shakes his head, blinks a few times, has a look around and says, 'Wait a minute! Mary, Martha, Jesus? What in the world do you think you're doing? I was up in heaven enjoying the company of angels, and you brought me back down to this rotten earth. What did you do that for?' " Is there any record of Lazarus reacting that way? Does this scenario make any sense to you?

On Faith: "Feed your faith, and your doubts will starve to death."

On Devotion: "When the Word goes in, sin goes out!"

On Revival: "The church is full of fashion, but no passion for souls. We express doubts and fears, but shed no tears, there are hundreds of interferes. God send us some intercessors!"

On Liberals: "When you throw a stick into a pack of dogs, the one that yelps loudest is probably the one you hit."

On Tongues: "You got a ghost for sure, but it ain't the Holy Ghost."

On TV:

"I dare you to take your idiot box and put it in the garage for one month, and the time you spend watching it, spend in prayer and Bible study . . .

Place your Bible on your TV, and see which you reach for most. For the self-righteous here who threw away your TV, put your Bible on the refrigerator . . .

You say 'I can't see what's wrong with it!' Of course you can't, blind people can't see! But pull your neutral brain out of the tube and put it where there is light, and I promise you, you will see!"

On Gossip:

"Whoever gossips to you, will gossip about you."

"It isn't hard to make a mountain out of a molehill–just add dirt."

"He who throws dirt loses ground."

On Truth: "Truth is stranger than fiction, but not nearly as popular."

On Christianity: "If you were accused of being a Christian and were brought to trial, would there be enough evidence to convict you?"

On Church Cooperation: "If you're busy rowing the boat, you don't have time to rock it!"

On Temptation:

"Most folk who leave a temptation behind, give it a forwarding address."

" 'No' is one of the few words that can't be misunderstood."

On New Birth: "Be born once, die twice. Be born twice, die once."

On Scripture: "A memory stored with Scripture is a bank that will never fail."

On Prayer: "The real secret of prayer is praying in secret."

On God: "It's not how much of God we have that's important. The question is, how much of us does God have?"

Leo Schreven

On the Second Coming: "God's prophetic time clock has no snooze button."

Favorite E. G. White Quote: "Five minutes would solve most problems people have been dealing with for years."

On Government:

"Don't steal; the government hates competition!"

"If pro is the opposite of con, then what is the opposite of progress? Congress!"

"If voting could really change things, it would be illegal."

"Rome wasn't built in a day . . ." That's because it was a government job.

On Marriage:

"A marriage may be made in heaven, but the maintenance must be done here on earth."

"A woman's heart is like a campfire. If you don't tend to it regularly, you will soon lose it."

"A man who has a Mercedes in his garage won't steal a Volkswagen off the street."

"Marriage is an investment that pays you dividends, if you pay interest."

On Success and Prosperity:

"The only place success comes before work is in the dictionary."

"The person who says it can't be done is liable to be interrupted by someone doing it."

"The difference between ordinary and extraordinary is that little 'extra.' "

"Success is a matter of your backbone, not your wishbone."

"If you're on the right track, you'll get run over if you just sit there."

"Success does not consist in never making mistakes, but in never making the same mistake twice."

"Success is a relative thing. The more success you have, the more relatives you meet."

"The person who is waiting for something to turn up might begin with his own shirt sleeves."

"I'd rather attempt to do something great for God and fail, than do nothing and succeed."

"What counts is not the number of hours you put in, but how much you put in the hours."

"To fail to plan, is to plan to fail."

On How to Know You're Getting Old:

"When everything hurts, and what doesn't hurt, doesn't work."

"When your address book contains only names ending with M.D."

"When your children look middle age."

"When your knees buckle and your belt won't."

"When you're 17 around the neck, 42 around the waist, and 99 around the golf course."

"When your back goes out more often than you do."

"When you sink your teeth into a vegeburger and they stay there."

On When It's Going to be a Bad Day:

"You call suicide prevention, and they put you on hold."

"Your birthday cake collapses from the weight of the candles."

"The bird singing outside your bedroom window is a buzzard."

General Daily Wisdom:

"Don't worry about what people are thinking about you, because they are not thinking about you. They are wondering what you are thinking about them."

"A committee meeting is usually a meeting of the bored."

"Why worry? Worry is like a rocking chair; it gives you something to do, but you wont get anywhere."

"Don't be afraid to ask dumb questions. They're a lot easier to handle than dumb mistakes."

Final Thoughts On . . .

Gay Rights: "The right to do something doesn't make it right!"

Animal Rights: "Killing two birds with one stone will usually result in hate mail from the Audubon Society."

UFOs: "Yes, I can prove there's intelligent life in the universe, because they stay clear of us!"

Other Books, Cassette Tapes, and Videos by Leo Schreven

Books:

Title: ***Now That's Clear!***

A 215-page book of Leo's Prophecy Seminars. Twenty-three chapters cover the prophetic message of truth with over 1,000 Bible verses, graphs, and illustrations. One of the clearest biblical books of truth available anywhere!

Price $7.50

Cassette tapes:

Title: ***Prophecy Seminar***

Twenty-four quality cassette tapes of Leo's live Prophecy Seminar in a vinyl case. Cassette tapes are approximately 70 minutes in length and include 23 tapes covering all major Bible prophecies and teachings of Jesus. Plus, Leo's conversion story!

Price $60.00 per set.

Videos:

Title: ***Prophecy Seminar***

Twenty-four video tapes of Leo's dynamic Walla Walla, Washington crusade. Broadcast quality utilizing three cameras, this video series comes complete with graphics and illustrations. The entire message of the truth is presented in a crystal-clear, powerful way. Each sermon is sprinkled with humor, but above all, each uplifts Christ and the cross. Thousands have been baptized as a result. Excellent for small home groups and churches. Youth and young adults love this series! Each tape is approximately 70 minutes in length.

Price $275.00 per set

Available at your Adventist Book Center
1-800-765-6955

For the convience of those attending Leo's seminars, these materials can be ordered by mail. Total your order and add ten percent (10%) for shipping and handling (international–15%). Washington residents add eight percent (8%) sales tax.

Make checks payable to and mail to:
Leo Schreven
PO Box 520
Kettle Falls, WA 99141